IT'S NOT QUIET ANYMORE

New Work
From the Institute of American Indian Arts

Senior Editors

Heather Ahtone
Allison Hedge Coke

Editors

Milton Apache
Esther Belin
Elias Funaro
Tommy Keahbone
Ruth Mustus
Rebecca Proffitt
Roland Thomas Jr.

IAIA Anthology Series:

New Work, 1989
Desire and Time, 1990
Masked Spirits, 1991
Voices of Thunder, 1992

For information:

Creative Writing Program
Institute of American Indian Arts Press
P.O. Box 20007
Santa Fe, NM 87504

ISBN: 1-881396-08-8

CONTRIBUTORS

RETURNING THE GIFT

Heather Ahtone

listening to their voices
of a hundred years
a woman crying
for her son lost to the world
knowing his spirit must wait
to get the embrace
her arms ache to give him
to unload the burden
she feels from returning the gift

i hear these women speak
women of my people
sisters in spirit
and i rise to the clouds   shouting
i must say how i am strengthened
by their words
prayers i have eavesdropped upon
honored by their thoughts
of my future and my daughters

these women
voices are silk
sliding through my pen as ink
and staining the tree i scratch on
they are human in flesh
but their spirits are not subject to the chains which
    bind their hands
i long to communicate to them
in their language of song
a sound i have only just learned
as i begin to form sentences of my very own

7

MOONLIT VISTA

Heather Ahtone

restless fingers twitching
what time is it
watch-vacant wrist says nothing
head turning to allow
eyes the horizon's view
against black
on a mountain
stoke the fire
and it won't be black
moon hiding behind a cloud
floating from behind the silhouette of trees
above my head
close to the fire
add another log   twigs
burn brighter at first
and die fast
die before the sun rises
from the crevice i saw yesterday
blanket tighter
while the others sleep sound
soundlessly
alone in my dreams
i awaken to feel
warmth
and wonder
the moon breaks from the cloud
creating shadows of light
between trees i cannot see
and turn the log
fire blinds me from the moon
singing a song from my grandmother
to keep my eyes open
moon falls to the mountain's other side
another log and twigs

and my head feels heavy
blue
black blue
sun is awake somewhere
sky is turning
toss another handful on the fire
awaken the day

BURIAL

Heather Ahtone

she dies speaking a language
i forgot to learn
before she said goodbye
when i could   might have understood
why she faced the sun
when we laid her to rest
on the hill next to her mother

IT'S NOT QUIET ANYMORE

Heather Ahtone

CAST:
Male
Female
Chorus

SETTING:
An undefined space with draped material forming the walls. There should be blocks up stage right forming at least three steps with the middle step being two blocks wide. Downstage left there should be a group of blocks wide enough for two people to sit on. The block formations should also be draped in fabric.

CHARACTERS:
MALE is dressed in jeans, white t-shirt, and barefoot. FEMALE is dressed in a flowing outfit made of a calico print cotton. It has a low, round neck, and tailored bodice, with full legged pants She should be able to move freely.

STAGE NOTES:
The chorus should be allowed to interact with the audience and the dancers with little inhibition. This will encompass walking into the audience, talking with audience members, crossing the stage, eating/drinking during the performance, etc. These actions are acceptable as long as they don't interfere with the theme of the production, which is disrespect.

FEMALE and MALE should be able to join the CHORUS in reciting the text as well as using physical noises to accent the silences. Unless stated, the CHORUS should be free to speak text individually or as a whole which will be determined in production rehearsals.

Though the text is broken to allow for stage directions, it should be read continuously. The text breaks are for visual cues only. Where there is not text, stage directions should be followed in silence.

TEXT	ACTION
before before the heaviness of my father within her before the heaviness of me within her before they called my name	*FEMALE is laying on her back on the middle section of the upstage right blocks. Her legs are raised and she is having birthing contractions. While the lights are black, the sounds of heavy breathing should be heard. CHORUS begins speaking while lights are out.*
i called her mother mother i called her inside i could hear her the sound of sleeping the sound of praying the sound of laughter the sound of eating the sound of burping	*Lights rise to a spot on FEMALE in labor.. MALE crawls from behind the rear blocks. MALE collapses below the blocks.*
the sound of breathing the sound of her heart beating the sound	*FEMALE goes into a contraction, then goes limp. MALE begins crawling to down stage*

the drumming of my
mother

as through draped material

*When MALE enters down
stage center, he begins
reacting as though hands
are grabbing him. He
should be moaning,
screaming, reacting in fear.
At the same time, FEMALE
should be descending the
blocks and reclaiming her
body. FEMALE will then
approach MALE with her
skirt spread to engulf him.
MALE will resist at first,
then succumb to her skirt.
Both will collapse.*

drumming the sound of a
beat
her beat
her drum
drumming
beating her drum
her hands
her drumming hands
her beating hands holding
her holding hands holding
my hands holding her
holding hands
holding her hands holding
my hands
my hands holding my head
her hands holding my head
beat in my head holding
her hands

*FEMALE will start creating
a rhythm with body parts
against the floor, against
her body, against any
props. These will begin
slowly, then become more
rapid. MALE will respond
as though in pain at each
beat. FEMALE will use the
entire performance space
to create this beating.*

13

hands holding my head
beating
hands holding my head
drumming
my hands holding her
hands
her hands holding my head
my head drumming
drumming my head
her hands holding my head
drumming

hands
fingers
fingers on my hands
hands on my fingers
fingers hold hands hold
arms
arms hold hands hold
fingers
arms hold toes
toes on feet
feet on toes
feet on toes on feet
feet on legs on toes
legs on feet on toes
toes on feet on legs
feet on floor and legs
legs on floor on feet
floor on hands on fingers
floor on hands and feet
floor on hands and legs
feet on floor on fingers
fingers on floor on feet
feet on floor are walking

MALE will begin trying to move to stop the beating by controlling his physical body parts as mentioned in text. The reaction to pain should not stop, merely become more animated with resistance. As MALE is able to control more body parts, he should then try to approach FEMALE to stop her rhythm making.

walking on floor on feet
toes on floor and fingers
fingers on face
face on fingers
face on eyes
eyes on face on fingers
mouth on fingers on eyes
fingers on eyes on face
fingers on eyes on my face
fingers on mouth on my
face
fingers on nose on my face

fingers on eyes on her face
fingers on nose on her face
fingers on mouth on her
face
fingers on fingers on her
hands
fingers on back and her
arms
arms on back of her arms
her arms on shoulder on
my back
her arms on shoulder on
my back
her arms and shoulder and
my back
my shoulders and her arms
and back

*When MALE is able to
attract FEMALE's attention,
he will then start exploring
her body without making
physical contact. FEMALE
is responding by being shy
of the attention. MALE is
slowly getting closer
physically.*

her hands and arms and
legs
her legs and arms and
hands

*MALE finally makes
contact with FEMALE's
hand. He begins waltzing
her around the dance
floor. FEMALE does not*

15

her hands on my arms her
legs
her legs and hands and
floor
her arms around the floor
her legs around the floor
my arm around her legs
around the floor
my legs around her arms
around the floor
our legs and arms
around the floor
the floor around our arms
and legs
around the floor our arms
and legs
legs and arms around the
floor

around the arms
around the legs
around the floor
our arms
our legs
the floor
around
legs
arms
floor
our hand
our arms
our toes
our legs
floor
around

*respond at first, then is
following the steps
enthusiastically. The pace
picks up slowly. MALE will
build pace until FEMALE
cannot keep up. FEMALE
will fall to downstage right
when she can no longer
follow.*

*After MALE has lost
FEMALE, he will begin to
dance out of control by
himself, finally attaining a
spin which will cause him
to fall. FEMALE will try to
straighten her dress and
gather her self up. She will
not move from her
position.*

16

the floor
hands
arms
toes
legs

our own
our own belonging (you)
our own needs (love)
our own wants (sex)
our own desires (money)
our wants & needs (love)
our wants & desires (sex)
our needs & desires
    (money)
are wants (love)
are needs (sex)
are desires (money)

When MALE has fallen, he will stumble over to FEMALE. He will try to persuade her to become physical.. FEMALE will resist and back into the downstage center. MALE will become more aggressively until he is physically restraining FEMALE.

artist ires
artist needs
artist wires
artist nails
artist hammers
artist paint
artist brush the paint
artist hammer the nails
hammer the brush
brush the paint
brush the nails
brush the paint
brush the nails
brush the paint
brush the pain
pain's a must

MALE becomes violent and begins raping FEMALE at down stage center. FEMALE should scream as a victim would, and should be looking to the audience for help. She should reach out physically towards the audience and CHORUS. The female members of the CHORUS should cover their eyes, while the male member should be looking to the audience for help as to what to do. He should be visibly troubled.

17

pain's a brush
pain's a hammer
hammer the pain
hammer the nail
nail the pain
nail the hammer
nail the hand
nail the brush
brush the nail
brush the face
hammer the face
hammer the nail
hammer the brush

brush the face
rush the face
rush the hand
rush the arms
rush the legs
touch the face
touch the arms
touch the legs
grab the face
grab the hands
grab the arms
catch the face
catch the hands
catch the arms
catch the legs

*When MALE has finished
raping FEMALE, he should
then start to walk away.
FEMALE will move to strike
MALE . MALE will turn and
begin beating FEMALE
violently. As the beating
builds, MALE will laugh.
slowly building to hysteria.
The beatings will end when
MALE is so hysterical, he
can no longer move..*

catch the race
catch the bands
catch the tribe
catch the children
catch the elders

*When MALE has stopped
beating FEMALE she will
step to the audience and
show them her bruises and
search for help. As she*

catch the women
catch the tribes
tribe catch the children
children catch the women
women catch the elders
elders catch the tribes
tribes of women
tribes of children
tribes of elders
dying off
tribes of women
dying off
tribes of children
dying off
dying off
killing off
killing dying off
dying killing off
killing off women
killing off children
killing off elders
killing off tribes
killing women
killing children
killing elders
killing tribes
killing men
killing myself
killing my mother
killing my father
killing my sister
killing my brother

*moves through the
audience, she will start to
hear a baby crying,
looking over her shoulder
to the stage. The baby's
cries will become louder
and louder until, she
returns from the audience
and picks up an invisible
baby from the front
blocks. While FEMALE is
moving through the
audience, MALE will be
moving hysterically
around the stage. MALE
will finally end up at the
rear blocks, which he tries
but cannot mount..*

killing
cutting
dissecting
chopping
slicing
dissecting
pulling apart
testing and dissecting
pushing and pulling
categorizing
elements and atoms
spinning and gravity
pulling the gravity
gravity spinning and
testing
dissecting and categorizing
cutting and testing
wondering which is
pushing and pulling
dissecting and testing
wondering which is
gravity spinning
wondering which is
falling down
dissecting and spinning
pulling and testing
falling down
wondering which is
categorizing
falling down
wondering which is
falling down
london bridges
falling down
wondering which is

When FEMALE picks up the baby she starts cuddling and playing with it. As she picks up the baby, MALE will start stepping in circle, heel-toe, circling the rear blocks and slowly forming larger circles. FEMALE is humming "London Bridges" to the baby. When MALE begins circling midstage, his steps will become interrupted with spasms. He must stagger trying to maintain the pace. FEMALE will then move to the rear blocks, oblivious to MALE, with the baby. When MALE is on the next to last circle, he will start crawling. The male CHORUS member will approach MALE to help him to complete the circles and rest on the front blocks. As he approaches the front blocks he will crawl into a fetal position and go limp.. Male CHORUS member will look to the audience for help and then to FEMALE. She should give no response. Male CHORUS member will return to the CHORUS position.

falling down
falling down
falling down
wondering which is
falling down
my fair lady

*When the text is
completed, FEMALE should
hum the lullaby once
completely under a single
spot..*

THE END

NATIVE AMERICAN THEATRE:
A Cultural Necessity

Heather Ahtone

Native American Theatre is a genre presently being defined. As an art form, it is crucial to the preservation and education of Native cultures. It retains the potential of becoming the most powerful tool in reclaiming, maintaining, and expanding our cultures

With such potential, there comes responsibilities. As Native theatre is developed, its innovators must address issues which affect and apply to Indian peoples in all the Americas, and which are crucial to maintaining our culture through the next 500 years and beyond.

We must make our voices heard as part of the human community to be able to tell our histories in our own words. We must preserve the oral traditions of storytelling, music, and dance which will educate Natives and non-Natives of our beliefs. We must address political issues which affect us today and unite our voices to withstand assimilation.

It is necessary to communicate our histories in our own words. For years, the story of the Natives has been told to Natives, as well as non-Natives, through a funnel which eliminates the facts surrounding the wholeness of our cultures. We must demand to be heard in order to address the fallacies taught as fact, not only to non-Natives, but to the Native children which reduces their interest and faith in systems that have existed longer than the systems being imposed through said education.

We must be able to present our pre-Columbus histories to our own people as valuable fact rather than myths of a savage and superstitious peoples. Communicating our stories in our own words will not only educate Native peoples but will also give us a sense of pride and belonging currently being subjugated with ignorance and shame. This subjugation is a method used by dominant society to weaken and control us enacted through the teaching of fictitious historical fact. The false history currently being taught in public schools removes our true histories and devalues our cultures.

By taking control of our own stories and not only documenting them, but recreating them through theatre, we will reclaim that history as a part of our identity. By strengthening our identity, we become human beings capable of affecting positive change for our individual selves as well as our individual cultures. This reeducation and valuation of our selves will empower us to reclaim and preserve our cultures.

Reclaiming our cultures through storytelling, music, dance, and dramatic performance is necessary. We would be documenting our stories in a way not alien to our cultures. Music, ceremonial and social dance, and the oral tradition have been a part of our cultures since our creation. Theatre encompasses these elements and presents them in a manner which communicates on emotional and intellectual levels. Theatre has the indisputable ability to affect peoples thoughts and beliefs, unmatched except in sacred ceremonies. This ability does not discriminate against race or creed, but affects all people.

Through theatre, Native people would be preserving our cultures and educating audience members, Native or not, as to who we are, where we came from, and why we are here. This defining of identity would enable Native people to act upon todays issues and to prepare for the forthcoming generations.

subjugating our own values. This voice would then be able to affect political change counter to the assimilation mode currently in practice.

We would be able to manipulate the current stereotype of a noble, savage, ignorant Indian into an image reflective of the sanctity of our people. The reclaiming of our identity and perpetuation of an honest representation would empower Native people to withstand the pressures to conform to dominant society's value system. This newly claimed identity would eliminate the need for Native individuals to use dominant society's remedies for shame and rebellion (i.e. alcohol and drugs). Individuals could make a personal choice regarding assimilation without the constant barrage of devalued, degraded culture.

By refusing assimilation, we would then disable the bureaucratic system used not only by non-Native people, but also adopted by tribal governments. Tribes would return to traditional systems of government which were not based on gender or monetary worth. Economic development would become unnecessary subject to the communal values practiced in most traditional customs. Power would be removed from financially driven politicians and rightfully returned to holy people in communion with the Creator. These people would be considered leaders as long as they acted on behalf of the people and not for a predetermined term of self-service.

Native people would become independent of support from unstable, unethical governments. They would become a united voice of indigenous cultures, demanding not only attention, but also respect and retribution. Without the necessity of government support, retribution could be accepted in a manner

This defining of identity would educate non-Natives about our histories and beliefs, thereby displacing ignorance with knowledge. When a person is able to understand other belief systems, he is more apt to respect those systems and their followers. It would be ambitious to suggest that every audience member would gain such
enlightenment every time, as well as foolish. However, it is undeniable that every audience member would be impacted at some level and possible communication channels would be created.

Through theatre, this communication would extend not only to non-Natives, but also to Native people. Communication would be established between disparate tribes recreating a system of exchange. Tribes would be able to share knowledge and information allowing for mutual development reminiscent of pre-colonialization. Not only would customs and practices be revived within tribes, but ceremonies would be shared as was ordained by the Creator in the beginning. Tribes that were near cultural extinction, not as determined by membership but by loss of traditional values, could be resuscitated. Tribes that have maintained their traditional identity could become catalysts for a Native revolution. An uprising against the devaluation imposed for 500 years. An uprising of strength impeding the progress of dominant society's values which cripple our political voice.

By cultivating our voice through theatre, we educate ourselves and others. This education would be removed of eurocentric values and disabling identification. We would be strengthening our voice and gaining the ability to express ourselves to non-Natives in a manner understandable to them without honoring those who have suffered or died from the effects of assimilation and genocide.

It is necessary for Native theatre to be developed as an act of cultural preservation and development. Without the stories of our creations and histories, we have no identity. Without the education of ourselves and others we will become remnants of extinct cultures, incapable of identifying ourselves as anything distinct from dominant society.

We will have lost beliefs and ceremonies that were given by the Creator to us in order to maintain the balance of life on the planet. We are responsible, not only to our past and future generations, but also to the planet to preserve the gifts given to us by the Creator.

A Native theatre would encompass presenting and preserving our stories as well as an arena for education and exchange. Native theatre would encompass the values of ceremony without violating the sanctity of our sacred teachings.

It is possible that Native theatre could be developed in a mindful manner respective of the responsibilities encompassed. It could possibly transform the Occidental view of what theater was meant to be. By respecting ourselves, we may well teach others to respect their own beliefs and create a global community of respecting communities and balance. Granted, this sounds far-fetched, but amazing things happen when people stand for themselves and unite for a mutual cause.

There is so much to be done, but as there is presently no criteria dictated on how Native theatre will be developed, there is free ground to pave without breaking through useless cement.

TAILPIPE...

Gino Antonio

Tailpipe   wire hung or
stupendously attached to invisible
high strung thick steel springs
broken windows cracked ones,too
windshields with the omniscient spider web
that only attracts
more flying rocks
sometimes   replaced by cardboard boxes
which once encased a Downy detergent bottle
or
the alternative, plastic
always gave the illusion of speed not capable of
with its flap in the wind
overloaded to its capacity but not here
everything is capable   especially
when most everything is held in place
by cables   big and small
the trunk
the lights
and, the hood   of its very own color
muddy Caddy's and drop-dead Dodges
all with snow tires encasing last year's air
which tries to escape   but cannot
because of the ever present little steel cables
bumper stickers shouting   " Frybread Power"
and the political ones that tell
everybody who tried to run for office in
1978   but I can't make it out because
of the mud
and trail of blackened gray smoke
full of dents   just gotta' give 'em names
I remember this big one   named it "BAD JIM"
given the morning after
after a good night at the 49 last year
the same night I showed off my studded gas cap

and saw a rag in its place   in the morning
Jesus hangs solemnly
the rear-view mirror is encrusted in fingerprints
One-Eyed Jacks lights the way
and broken taillights only attract
expensive nightmares   flashing red lights
backfires that resembles a giant's sneeze
and carries like an annoying voice in
Echo Canyon
hubcaps that have grown invisible
or   have found sanctuary somewhere on US 66
better yet
traded jobs as a new roof
for a prairie dogs humble home
Oh
the sounds of soleless brake shoes   stretched
squeeking joints   and   screaming eyesore
                    slowing down
is
music to the ears of my bulging thumb
on this cold January morning
on my way to get BACK   the carrier
of   " BAD JIM"

THE RED MAN'S HAVEN

Gino Antonio

The Red Mans Haven
as
portrayed
in
words

was meaningful
was taken   and taken...

taken until
YOU took and stripped
away   MY Pride
Joy
Representation
Respect
Integrity

Institutionalized
with YOUR
portrayed words   full of
meaningless
Words only   (Empty Ones)
Only words to
power YOUR

promiscuous POSITION
      pregnant POCKETS
            pimping POLICIES

Will YOU continue   to Ban   use YOUR
2 Dimensional Black Tape   on
OUR savorous tenacious tongue
        to cover up the
Red Tape   and YOUR White lies

                    to play with
         OUR   Resources   gaining
         interest on YOUR
                    So Called prestigious scholarship
         in YOUR game called Monopoly
                    to feed and fill
         Established Stomachs   with

Freshly killed Lobster
         Prime Cut Steaks n
                    confectionary Fish Eggs

         as to prolong YOUR PayDay
         While
         Cringing Craving Stomachs
         are filled to a minimum with
         Commods   and
         Embezzled fruits from friends
                    to cater to the
         Institutionalized American Immaculate Agers
         Born Agains n Wannabees   recruited
         to Reteach   Ranting Raging Traditional
                    TONGUES
         bastardizing the Medicine Culture
         with   visiting
         Synthetic Shaman
         Packing plastic Cards
   to Pay   I mean to pray   I mean to pave
         THEIR way into OUR Sacred Domain
                    to see the NEEDLESS   deaths
         of Spirits born to soar
         from Season to Season
         Year to Year
         OUR Friends that
         heard   YOUR Same

Portrayed Words
which
came from
Tunnel Vision MOUTHS

When will YOU wake up?   When will You listen?
        When will...

        I will share MY thought   Today
        Keep YOUR Tongue outta MY mouth

                TODAY'S RED MAN'S HAVEN
                "THE INSTITUTE OF America's Indians ART"

THE WHIRL

Gino Antonio

The whirl   in my fingertips
The brown in   my eyes
The twinkle in my   toes
The   motion   in my stride
The strand in   my head
The ripple in my   brain
The   thought in my heart
The eruption in   my mouth
The wave in   my   ears
The   scar in my   muscle
The travels in   my blood
The dream   in my chest
The   bounce in   my butt
The laugh in   my stomach
The   hunger in   my   bite
The vibrato   in   my throat
The hide   in my skin

The sweet   in   my sweat

The empty in my pockets
The   song in my   lap
The   thump in my groin
The   happiness   in my callouses
Little Child in my arms
Sleeping in my palms
Listen to   my words
A   long   time   ago
  before you were even a thought
     These
     were the things you granted   me
     graciously   except one

          An emptiness

32

without this fatidic void
the crux in my being would never experience
Flaming   Vigilance
...Untamed flame loses no luster when freedom
shines poetic
resurgence

ONE SATURDAY NIGHT

Gino Antonio

We were under orders to stay in our make-
shift bunkers that night. Message came over the
radio reporting sights of the enemy in our
perimeter. The shelling would stop and start again.
When it was silent, you could hear grown men
crying or screaming in pain. Sometimes I wish I
could have done something to help, but you just
couldn't tell with the enemy around. When the
bombs were hitting all around us, it reminded me of
the summer thunderstorms. I remembered being a
scared little kid in Grandpa's lap during the storms.
He used to hold me and tell me stories about the
thunder and how it wasn't bad, but good if you made
it that way. He then showed me how to pray to the
thunder and rain to ask for protection. I
remembered the prayers and made my own for all of
us in this war.

I double-checked the radio and decided to get
some sleep before anything changed. I needed some
rest and asked my friend to stand watch. My friend
was (laugh) my own security guard assigned to me.
It got real quiet, nobody wcrying or screaming and
nothing was moving, my eyes got real heavy and I
let out a slow breath. I looked up, then noticed the
full moon. It looked funny; it was orange and
seemed to be so close, too close. That's the last thing
I remembered before I fell asleep.

When my eyes closed, I felt real peaceful. It
felt like there was no war going on at all. I was
asleep, but I was standing at the opening of a cave. I
looked at myself and I had military clothes on. I
started to look back up and I heard someone singing
to me. It was coming from the cave and it was a
medicine man singing. A fast wind came to me and
knocked me forward, telling me to go towards the
song. I started walking and the cave got darker. I

was not scared and kept walking even though I couldn't see. I just followed the words of the song echoing off the walls. My ears were happy and my legs slowly kept going.

I kept walking and listening. The song got louder as I kept getting closer. Soon, my eyes saw a bright light glowing. It looked like the early, twilight dawn from back home. I stopped and I opened my arms and brought the air into me. Four times I breathed it in. I closed my eyes and I said a prayer. I was about to bless myself when I looked down and I had my ceremony clothes on, and my hair was long again. The fast wind came again whispering in my ear and soothing my eyes. I walked forward again and started to hum along with the song. The glowing light showed me pictures on the rock and the light got stronger and the song got louder. I could smell the smoke of a fire close, real close.

The fire came in view real fast. There was a medicine man singing by the fire. He lookied like an old man, but I couldn't tell.He motioned me to come over. I walked over and he sat me down. He put his hand in the fire and brought out some redhot coals. His other hand reached into a pouch and he pulled out something that I couldn't see. He put it into the coals and smoke rose from his hands. He put more of that thing into the coals and some into the fire. There was more smoke and he picked up an eagle feather fan and fanned me with the smoke, my whole body. I closed my eyes and breathed in the sweet smoke and I could feel my body get stronger with each word from his song and the sudden pounding of a drum. He kept singing and playing and my body stood up automatically and I began to walk back out.

I was strong again, and I could hear my Grandfather. He was telling me, "You are Navajo. You are strong. You will come back to you, you are protected."

I walked back out. As I got closer to the entrance, I had my military clothes back on again. I noticed something in the palm of my hand as I looked at the storm clouds and lightning in the distance.

I suddenly woke up to a loud roar. I thought it was a shell that hit close by, but it was beginning to rain. I didn't notice it, but my friend was yelling at me. He was saying, "What the hell are you doin' goin' out there? What, you tryin' to count coup on the enemy, you crazy Indian? Don't do that shit again."

I didn't know I had walked out of the bunker when I thought I'd dreamed of being in the cave, but I felt different. My body wasn't tired anymore, and I had strength again. I listened to what my friend said and took a deep breath. A strong breeze hit my body and a shiver went down my spine. I rubbed my arm and that's when I noticed this black arrowhead in the palm of my hand.

"Daddy, will something like that ever happen to me?"

"I hope you don't have to, and pray that you won't."

"But Grandpa, I want to have a dream like that."

"Listen to your Grandfather, son. We don't need no more wars. That dream came from a ceremony your Grandfather was having over my clothes while I was away fighting so I could come home safe."

"I promise, you will have a dream like that some day. You will have a strong dream. I will teach you how to pray like my grandfather showed me and your grandfather will teach you holy songs. You are our future. Don't forget about the things we teach you AND never be afraid because you have to show these things to your new baby brother.

CAST

Milton Apache

Today is the loneliest day of my life
because Sunday casts cold grey shadows.
And clouds move fast over unending days

Mocking birds chirp, (A trilogy to my saddened state.)
Last night I walked through the cemetery
With the full moon capturing a boy
sitting in an empty room.
Filled with a disturbed gaze
he sets his house on fire
A thick fog burrows into the boys nose and mouth
as he wallows down.

I stand from my sitting place
blood rushes to my head
White flash, mind fades to blank,
Gravity renders me down again.

The boy wants to sleep, and he does.
And he will dream of
the night swallowing the sun
and trapping himself in a spider's web.
The web has returned for the sixth time.

Sirens and flashing lights
lets a comatose loose grip
and permits the boy to jump
over and off the balcony, facing the ocean.

I come to and notice myself in a nearby lake
halfway under.

His lungs burn, saltwater punctures through his lungs.

And I used to laugh, to hide these eyes of pain
but nothing is lost in these drops, that drop into
a plain turquoise pool.
And now I dont smile at all

HE READS MINDS
Milton Apache

A figure was standing on the bridge. Not to the left,
    not to the right But in the middle.
He wants to jump because he fears.
Fears what ? you may ask.
He fears me he fears you
he believes if he stays he will live
and if he jumps he will die

Somewhere in a nearby neighborhood.
A boy has an eerie feeling. He feels   his neck snap.
Two blocks away from him,
 a car screeches into a collision

The boy falls away into the fetal position
He explains that on 142nd St. was a brick building
with a sign that reads Enjoy Coca Cola.
A purple sedan , a person and her carriage
As the boy finishes his sentence. He dies.

The woman dies at that instant. She also lays
in the fetal position, with a broken neck.
The baby in the carriage ends up on the hood.
In the process of the collision, the babys eye becomes
    eliminated.
He cries, because he loses something
and it's not his eye.

The figure on the bridge   now climbs on the rail.
Someone approaches. It's a curious child.
Who is intrigued with what the man is doing
The man screams as he hits midpoint
between the bridge and the rocky shores.

The aroused boy follows
Freefalling the boy notices a rope
at midway he notices a man.

DREAMSONGS FROM THE UNDERGROUND
Milton J. Apache

Aaaaaaaaaaaaaaaaa!

Aaaaaaaaaaaaaaaaaa!   BOOM BOOM BOOM
                                            BOOM

Aaaaaaaaaaaaaaaaaa!   BOOM BOOM BOOM
                                            BOOM

Aaaaaaaaaaaaaaaaaa!   BOOM BOOM BOOM
                                            BOOM

He enters with a dreamsong
                                   He creeps upon
                                            unconsciousness.

Then enters toward limbo
                                   There was a light

at the far end of the street
                                   A solitary gas lamp,
                                            Flickers.

On the other side of the street
                                   is a warehouse wall.

He is standing in a gateway,
                                   leading to some stables,
                                            between

a few houses, a red brick
                                   boarding school. She was
                                            lying
                                   on her back

one hand nearly touching the
        gate.
                                   Her black straw bonnet was
                                            lying

Nearby, Her dress was pushed up

almost to her waist.

Pssst hey lady come feel the dullness
of my blade inside your gut. The man grabs
her by the arm and swings her toward him.
Blade meeting pelvis, then penetrating
through bone about three inches past.
Her abdomen muscles, contracts, retracting
bring the dull object in and out.

Flaps of skin, flesh dangling, as blade
jabs to perform a jagged work of art.
She opens her mouth to scr...   Aaaaaaagghghhh

She looses her words
somewhere between the dimensions
 of a split second
and a severe stretching itself
about eight inches toward her vertebrae.
She reaches for her neck, grabbing his hand.
Somewhere in the struggle her bonnet
comes whirling to the ground. Moving loose dust
aside landing near blood drops.

She sees her reflection grow larger
landing on the curdled blood
figure becomes abstracted.
In her possessions were a comb,
a white handkerchief, a broken
mirror.

As red eyes burn through the hole
                                        They watch a little boy
comb his hair.

blackened
attic. A breeding ground for hybrid

floor and dust, slithering, howl

Bodies of skin and face dismember

in a corner. First clawing

his aortic vein.

It, stands hunched in a

bodies of skin and face
   grinding

-ing, into an ecstatic
   remorse.

a terrified child
   crouching

chewing, then
   separating

Life enters the realm of
   non-
   existence.

In a small desert
   community.
A little girl is running
   home in
the rain. Lightning
   strikes
thunder follows.
The beat pounds faster
in her chest.
Her pace is quickened
   palms began to perspire.
Mudwater splashes on new
   black
sandals, leotards and
   white

. . . dress

                              treading through water
                              shes overcome by a jolt
                         and staggers
                              seeing image in water.
                         The raindrops fall beside
                              her.

  The day before, I remember

                              tick, tick, tick, tick, tick,
                                   tick.

her giving me a carnation, a hug

                              tick, tick, tick, tick, tick,
                                   tick.

a jellybean

                         tick, tick, tick.

On Broadway Boulevard

                         sits an old fraternity house.
                              A boy

enters the room

                         lies down on the cold
                              linoleum tiled

floor. His roommate sits up

                         in his bed and sends the
                              boy a

shallow
smile.

                         The boy stands, exits room

toward the bathroom. He stands

                         at the furthest urinal,

                          urinating he hears a squeak

from a stall door open

                         closing.

The boy feels uneasy so he

concentrates on his shadow on
the

wall,

he glances upward and
notices

there is only one light working

in the dim bathroom.

He walks briskly to the door.

He touches the handle and
gives a
heavy breath. He walks out
and hears

the unpleasant squeak   open

and   close.

The boy turns and notices a

contour cipher facing him. He
runs to his

room,   locks the door,

runs to the corner of the room,

and sits.

He grabs a handful of hair,

pulls,

he whimpering and repenting

as the perpetual rapping on the
door

forces his face to the floor.

The man makes his way into the
room.

The boy feels the coolness

of a magnum 45 on his temple.

tick,   tick,   tick.

It moves toward his heart
and

is fired.

Tick,   tick,   tick.

The rain starts up again
I look out the window.
The droplets splash
  on the pane.
I see my mother sitting
at the table

sniffling and wiping her tears.
I ask

Aaaaaaaaaaaaaaaah
Aaaaaaaaaaaaaaaah
Boom Boom Boom
Aaaaaaaaaaaaaaaah

      (Bodies and faces move
        wildly
       and scream loudly.)

Why is it so gloomy when it rains?
She answers, God is sad and crying.

Children!   Children!
I have the answer
I know the way
He is Lord and Savior
call him deliverance
  Because
  He died on the cross
  So you can live by the
    cross
  and Satan
    conspirator of good
you will die by the
  Flames of Hades.

Aaaaaaaaaaaaaaaaaaa
aaaaaaaaaaaaaaaaaaa
aaaaaaaaaaaaaaaaaaa

aaaaaaaggggghhhhhgh

Arise!   Arise!
Flames of Hades Arise!
Proclaim your vile presence
Blister and melt my face

(N.W.O. grabs priest and
    beats him.)

from existence.
This
Run!   Run!
Run! from them

(points to priest.)

Come to us

The New World Order
is now   in   effect.
You hate your present
Government?

Lies, Lies, Lies
We tell you
your truths.
When you sleep We enter.
To give you drugs of escape
So come to us
THE HOUSE OF AGGRESSION.
Lacquer your sensitivity
We will have   Victory.

Through the eyes of our loved ones
Through the fears of our most hated.
Ourselves.
Smash violence
With violence.
The breeze feels good
   as I stand at my window
I feel the tornado   Will
satisfy my dying need.

                              of acceptance

Drug me up while sleeping
and when I wake
reason will write
poems of me.
I can write poems

of reason. He stands
in the twilit renaissance
of the setting sun.
Waiting to be killed
enlightenment   weightless
it ponders,
the red demon
of sub-& conscience
run wild and scattered
as I ink them together
I create a chaotic poem
of green rivers
interlocking
lavender pools of clouds
swimming adjacent

on my cuticle

I sit and watch the face
of the purple haze
I cant see. Eyes burn
with cool waves
of turpentine

stuck to my face

is a palm of a hand
is it mine?
four   eight   twenty,
hands crawl over my body
and this world must be destroyed
                          He follows the red
                          and yellow walls

                              of these New Mexico plateaus
                              valleys with creeks and
                                        aspen turning
                              yellow and a magentic
                                        orange.
                              some where between the
                                        crevices
        of reality,   settles a dirt path that
                                        weaves into
                              and out of these mountains.

he comes to a halt.
in a clearing covered with browning grass   an old motor vehicle is
                                                being driven by some
                                                one.

He sees himself running alongside the
 car.
With four other happy children.
he wasnt.
five and a half years earlier
 he hadnt existed
A mishap.
and a couple older kids beat him.
Just so hell live up to his
name. A bloody bastard.
And so now he runs after a car.

four boys

Lost in the years of their youth.

HIS SATIN NIGHTS

Milton Apache

Oh father!
will you ever stop?
You have your fun
of quivering eyes bloodshot
piercing through me
like a shiny sword
with a gold trimmed
handle.

While I have my nightmares
of writing you with reflections
of candle lights in mirrors.
Decorated around the room
were porcelain pots
big enough to shatter over my head
CRASH!
light! white!
white! white light!
almost seems colorful
before falling on our burgundy carpet.

Night two whickering flames
and the cold February breeze
kept me awake all night to avoid
You creeping up to my headboard
with hideous laughters following
the trail of your hot breath

You slither your belt from its loops
and fold it in half
my aching hands can do nothing, but fold
and my busted lips can say nothing
but a prayer for you.

SHADOW

Milton J. Apache

Always Remember our drive
down Sunset boulevard
Never to return to this world
Dream day and daydreams with whisps
of saltwater breeze
Embroidered silk
        red roses
sets the dusk to a mango colored sunset.
On top of nightfall, city lights
and subtle starry-eyed nights
draped with black curtains.
reading poetry through cracked
windshields   whispering rain d r o p s
s l a p p i n g   window sills.
Violent ticks of hypnotic tocks and
wrapped in sheets of purple, pink, and blue
Thrown from cliffs, ledges and
California was beautiful this time of year

CABAL DEVOURES KISSES

Milton J. Apache

Night falls   followed by day   break.
While Springtime calls for the rain washed valleys.
and for the butterfly passing through windows and
gardens furnished with mahogany trees.
Apple orchards turn from a plum purple to
a blossomed pink, trimmed with white edges.

A woman has been seated, and her son is walking
     through the garden.
He crosses a little stream, and heads toward the apple
     orchard.
Suddenly, she announces that he should not be there.
But it's too late, the thorns of the nearby cactus,
grabs the boy on the legs, torso, and arm.

The woman can't get up to save the boy, because
her tongue is caught between her teeth.
She can't open her mouth to scream, if she does
a spider will make a web between her opened mouth
allowing the butterfly to become caught.

The boy moves, but the thorns stake their claim
into the boys blood soaked leg.
He yells   hoping for some assistance.

But howling wolves drown his plea for help.
They are feasting on a butterfly, that has
landed on an iris petal to rest. Sharp teeth
crawl into the butterfly's head and side.
As the butterfly becomes devoured the pack of wolves
     lay
on the grass and stare hungrily at the boy who is now
     frightened.

A circular wave of motion, intertwine hands
    a right and a left
This reminds the boy of butterflies, weaving into Lilac
    bushes
The only thing that remains now, is the pungent smell
of the purple flowers.

Trying to escape, the cactus clings the boy even harder
The boy screams, just as he remembers the woman
laying on the ground.

Across the stream, the spiders web
recovers the butterfly that had his leg caught, but
through his struggle the butterfly relapses, only to
    become restrained.
The woman is facing upward, to the boy it means
    nothing.
Jesus, come down, you're the only one who seems to
    care.

Howling wolves cry in the distance. Over the moors
beyond the countryside, lay between two ridges.

The indigo skyline
brushes the mountains. The mahoganies and apple
    trees
lose their brilliance, and flowers lose their prism glow.
The spectrum of rays decease to a cold grey.

LETTERS TO FATHER

Milton J. Apache

Slumber into daybreak 6:42 a.m.

Red aurora passes through and over
houses.
Portraits of starving men and women on
a flight of tie-dyed stairs,
knowing no other fate, but to go up and devour.
Enter sleep in black and white.

Meanwhile in C-30.
A desolate room cold and clammy,
stores an abandoned child.
With no signs of assurance
the boy is battered and bruised.

A family stigmatized by congenital insanity.
The New York Times.

A HARD-BITTENED FACE

Milton J. Apache

I see you smile, and it makes me wonder
is it real or a phasade of your childish character.
And I enjoy watching people smile and laugh
because then I know how miserable I am.

A twist of events make my stomach churn
So I say, "Give me another with a twist of lime.
        To go with my twisted life."
This is what makes me sick with laughter.
Because it's a twisted pun, all around.

I knew when I said I loved you
I'd have to eat my words.
And love is a repulsive taste.

And I see the words that make me happy
dripping from the tip of your tongue.
Here let me cut it off
this will fulfill me.

I might even smile for once
just to show you
the wrinkles forming
at the bottom of my nose
extending to the sides of my mouth.

Tonight may be my last
and if not, the coin will
still be flipping   waiting to land
on something, anything.
I anxiously outstretch my hand.
The anticipation is killing me
and may as well.

Instead of letting it tickle
on the hard concrete, or
gravel covered pathway. if they still exist.

Sitting alone in a park bench
I tell myself never let anyone
in again. You didn't listen
the first, second and the third.

I hear him calling, the voice is
coming closer and more distinct.

A person is walking down the path
stands by the bench.
He happens to notice my eyes
and asks if I'd been crying.

I smile clench my pen
jab him in the eye
and kick him in the balls.
I send hi on his way,   down.

He sits on the ground
lungs grasping for life support.
None found, and I comply with him,
"I'm just trying t reassure myself
death is on my side."

And now I know
it's as clear as the air that chokes me
"STOP!   STOP! WAIT PLEASE THE COIN HASN'T
     LANDED YET."

I'M NOT SORRY, GRANDAPPLE
Geraldine Barney

Alizarin Crimson drips
     through the base of her existence
Trickles of red
     sent
to submerge the Beauty Way
     But red   her strength
a color the Grandapples assumed would choke her
   destiny
     But
the color
     now maroon
has dried an unpleasant stench
     above their foreheads, on their skulls.
     "Asdáá Kin Lichíí níí," she shouts.
     "That is I.
     Woman of the Red House.
     Clan of the east!"

A HOME BETWEEN THE EARTH AND SKY

Neilwood Begay

I conceive visions former and past
elapsed memories
they are 50s aqua blue
with white rice
weeds spread over flat plateau
and even a dirt road
These primitive images
circle around an early Spring
pebbles fill
two engraved trails running parallel
over, around, and down
this philosophical early Navajo road

Around the back of me
my spine feels and sees
there are nine houses
one dwelling stores mementos from the 60s
one other holds 70s pictures
those are mine

What happened back then
that I should have stayed
there at your home
Where red dots on free sneaker shoes
meant that I was either right or wrong
Shoes, and red lint staged chile in the air
My younger brother and I want to know
what happened then
that I reversed the sides of my shoes
and asked you
if they were right or if they were wrong

Between the earth and sky
what is this veil that puts an eclipse

over my mood
What had happened
That I should have stayed there with you
there at your home

Your home
and in your home
I still feel rusted black paint chipping
away from metal bed frames
One flat panel or plate
spiral and twirl in a royal design
and you made it a home inside of me
before breakfast
before the first school bus
there on the plateau

My home
and maybe my home
for one night, one evening
I remember that evening too
my brother must remember just as well
What had happened
that we chased chile in the air
smelled it on our finger tips and
release it in to the 6pm sunlight
through old wooden panes
then hugged one caging bed frame
on each end
and watched the flames burn
as we listened to you

A home
and in a home
this parable pushes its way up
from beneath boxes filled with bags of free rice

rice
pebbles
roads
another 50s aqua blue

YOUR SPIDERWEB BROKE TODAY

Neilwood Begay

Your Spiderweb broke today
dropped the contents
your possessions
to the ground
to the ground
a screaming demon woman
a laughing goat
a squirrel that sprawled as it hit the ground
the ground
and many more of your belongings
to the ground
to the ground
still leafing
still falling

I WANT A NEW MOUNTAIN

Neilwood Begay

Moving around these confined spaces of a green
        room
I see all these numerals and letters
reading only the strongest numbers and words
because they are the only ones I know.
It might be that I still can't see washed out ink spots
representational of mountains
that I can't believe in anything new.
But it could also be my false assumption to assume
that black is the only match to the nostalgic faded
        shades of brown.

I sympathize, weakly inspecting the circles of glass
over my brown eyes.
There isn't anything that I can do
I erroneously conclude.
Still I support my bend that could insanely roll me
        on a sensitive side of my frame
if it weren't for the logical mind of some long ago
        man.
It is only a thought of mine,
but why couldn't I possess his brain?
Then I would be able to build a dispassionate red
        house
that would contrast the one dark image on this side
        of the mountain.

ONE LEAF, ONE SEED
Neilwood Begay

A tree
like the one that grows
inside my head
my mind
a tree
like the ones in my body
the veins that are printed
one red
one blue
all over me, you and them
A tree
that blossoms with leaves
grows, flowers and leaves seeds
a tree
sleeps, awakens, lives and falls
a beautiful pain
that grows and grows
until
A tree
like the one that lives inside of me

PUBERTY

Margaret Behan

Magett was real curious if her and her older sister Umillnet were going to have babies.

Magett was a chubby jolly thirteen year old. Umillnet was a petite fifteen year old, a late bloomer. They lived three miles west of Watonga, Oklahoma.

On Magett's birthday, May 12, 1939, she wanted to know if her and her sister will have babies. She remembered that old lady Dog Woman was like a fortune teller, she knew the old lady lived in town, but didn't know exactly where.

In the evening while washing supper dishes Ma get convinced umillnet to look for Dog Woman after school.

Umillnet said, "I'm scared. I heard Dog Woman was like a witch."

Magett answered, "We will never know for sure, until we meet her, huh?"

"Please, I want to know the unknown, can we please?"

Umillnet finally agreed by making her eyes big, and nodding her head yes.

Magett took it upon herself to tell her father they were going to be late from school that next day. He nodded his head yes and didn't question them. Magett anxiously went to bed. Umillnet did her usual thing. She read a few chapters of *Little Women* before going to sleep.

The next morning Magett jumped up out of bed and yelled with excitement and went over to Umillnet's corner of the room.

"Pevee Woonott (good morning) Big Sister." Magett ran to the kitchen and began fixing breakfast oatmeal. Umillnet was slow, dragging her feet. They ate, ran to the Whirlwind Country School. After school they got a ride to town with one of the teachers. They went to the section of town where the Cheyenne lived in a cluster of cabins. At the first cabin they came to they knocked on the door. Junior Star answered and directed them to Dog Woman's cabin.

"I'm scared, let's go home please."

"No, we can't now, come on."

"You are such a scaredy-cat."

Magett knocked on the door, they could smell liver and onions cooking. A tall, slim pretty old lady with her braids tied together in the back of her head, her glassy eyes piercing at them. In a gruff voice--

"We want to know if we are going to have babies?"

Dog Woman laughed. She was so tickled she invited them in to eat. Cheyenne custom is when you go to their home to visit you sit down to eat. They did. There was no talk while they ate. They finished while the girls washed the dishes. Dog Woman instructed them: "Go and get me a set of Rocky Mountain Oysters and come back and see me."

Magett looked disappointed: "Where are we going to get bullballs?"

'That is your problem, you get them if you want to know if you all are going to have babies."

Dog Woman pushed them out of her house, slamming the door.

"Ha ha ha, bullballs! Bullballs!"

"Little sister, now what?"

"Where are we going to get them?"

"This is crazy!"

"People are going to laugh at us when they hear this."

Magett already thinking Uncle is the kind of guy that can do anything. So they walked toward home. Uncle's house was across from the school. Uncle and Esther had six kids all in steps. Umillnet could see what Magett was thinking.

"Uh oh, this is embarrassing."

Magett had a determined look on her face.

She knocked on the front door. Esther answered.

"Hi girls, come on in, supper is almost ready."

They went in and sat on the couch quietly.

"What do you girls want?"

Quickly, Magett answered--"Nothing, we just came to visit."

Esther knew the girls didn't like her kids. She was curious why they were there. Magett got up and went into the kitchen to help Esther set the table.

"Where's Uncle?"

"Uncle and the boys went to get wood."

Just as she said that, Uncle and the boys came storming in.

"We're hungry."

They washed their hands at the same time in the wash basin.

We all sat down to eat hamburger patties, fried potatoes, and biscuits. Umillnet thought to herself, onions again, and the kids are getting on my nerves. She gave up the embarrassing idea and wanted to see how her little sister was going to handle it. Magett buttered up to Uncle.

"Magett, tell me what you want so I can rest."

"Uncle, let's go outside, this is private."

Umillnet held her breath, then heard Uncle crack-up. He came in.

"Girls better get home."

Umillnet ran to where her sister was. They walked home quietly. As they were about to reach the front door, Umillnet asked, "What did Uncle say?"

He would keep an eye out for them. He wants the both of us to baby sit his brats for a weekend so he and Esther can practice up on their stick game tricks. Umillnet yelled, "Oh, look at what you've done--just forget it. It is stupid!"

They went into the house. Their father asked what all the loud noise was outside.

"We were just playing."

Their father said, "Supper is on the table."

At the same time they said, "I'm not hungry."

He asked, "Where did you eat?"

"Uncle's. We ate onions twice."

"Who cooked onions?"

"Esther."

"She must sure like onions."

"Shush! Umillnet."

They washed the dishes, cleaned up the kitchen and went to bed. Umillnet buried herself in her book to escape her little sister.

"Umillnet, wouldn't it be neat if I had a baby girl that looked like me?"

"Shut up! Enough! Enough, go to sleep."

Many weeks passed, school was out. All of a sudden Charles came running to the house. In between his huffing and puffing, he was laughing.

"My daddy wants you girls."

"Hurry up."

Magett ran out of the house calling Umillnet.

"Come on."

"No."

Uncle was butchering a bull a rancher had an accident with. The rancher gave the bull to Uncle. Uncle handed a knife to Magett saying, "Cut them off, don't just stand there."

Slowly she began to cut the hide that linked the patch. Charles handed her a piece of rag to put them in, "Come back and tell us. Remember our deal."

After all that wait, now everything was happening. She had the jewels that are the key to her curiosity. She was in a daze, wondering what the Old Lady Dog Woman was going to actually do with these things. She remembered Umillnet to find her and go to Dog Woman's as quickly as she could. Finally they reached Dog Woman's house. Dog Woman already saw them, her curiosity had built, too. As soon as they got there she commanded them to build a fire out by her wood pile. They hurried. When the fire was burning well, she took the tied rag bundle, opened it and cut apart the pair of balls, handing one to Umillnet, and the other to Magett. Dog Woman said, "At the same time both of you throw them into the fire and watch which one is yours, and tell me if it pops."

They watched very carefully. Magett's popped. She screamed happily, jumping up and down, clapping her hands. Umillnet's did not pop.

"What happened?"

"Magett is the one that is going to have babies and Umillnet won't--but Magett's first baby she will give to you."

BRINGING HANNAH HOME

esther g. belin

we brought hannah home today
in afternoon sun with a crisp chill in the air
on a hill overlooking the bay.

two women with a child and a shovel and a frozen
    placenta wrapped in aluminum foil placed in a red
    plastic bag.
hannah was brought into this world
some say fourth others say fifth
five days before.
before we brought her home.

the weekend of rain softened the earth
but the cold discouraged the shovel from denting more
    than the surface.
i dug into the earth.
the ground weakened beneath the strength i put into
    the shovel
pounding the ground
smooth and moist at first
then cold and solid.

pounding the ground
warmed my arms.
i thought good thoughts for hannah and her mother
and prayed for us all.
remembering those who have passed on and those to
    be born
and i thought of my children to be born
and i thought of my father who has passed on.

breaking into the cold ground
i thought of the day we brought my father home.
the winter of navajoland had frozen the ground
and the earth chipped like ice   slivers of crunchy cold
    beneath our feet.

our bodies warmed by our work.
and the earth chipped like an old tree being chopped
    taking hours to finish.
our bodies tired from our work.
and the earth piled high beside the hole like the
    clouds and just as fluffy.
our bodies natural returning to the ground.

i dug into the ground.
digging out earth that would nourish hannah.
digging out life that would embody hannah.
and soon a small hole appeared four feet deep.

there we stood
two women with a child and a shovel and a frozen
    placenta wrapped in aluminum foil placed in a red
    plastic bag.
the frozen mass of
tissue and blood
was placed in the small hole
by hannah's mother.
and i felt her heat
tissue and blood
squatting with bloodied hands and cold earth
bringing hannah home.

2 + 2 = TOO MUCH

esther g. belin

I.
twice in the last two days
i drive a different man home
sleepy
exhausted from the energy put into a man

II.
amused by his handsome smooth face
talk to him with my eyes
smiling pretty at me from across the table
me smiling pretty back when he pours beer into my
    glass
smiling pretty still
feeling the lazy of the beer
mr. pillow talk
i wanna fall asleep right on your chest
mr. pillow talk just keeps smiling pretty at me from
    across the table
mr. pillow talk with nice hands
lean fingers caressing his beer glass
bringing it to his lips
smiling pretty
his face pretty and smooth
i wanna touch it
cup it with my hand and touch the prettiness
let him drink my touch
my touch too hard spills beer
mr. pillow talk with nice hands gets a rag from the bar
mr. pillow talk with nice hands also has a nice ass
nice ass
nice smile
nice night.

III.
the second man
shows age on his face
smiling in ways i remember

with dancing eyes boyish dewy-new
smiling in ways to make me care
with grin well-deep
and we talk
eyes first
scanning the years
then nothing
cuz memory won't let me go any further
holding each other
the heat once there
is now lost
in the well of his grin.

C'MON BABY TELL ME

esther g. belin

for my brown/red/mutual/baby sister who knows how to talk/love/hide/inspire me

I.
hi my name is consuela
i wear a veil to hide
my yellow teeth
stained by imported
$3.25 a pack cigarettes

the veil of protection covers me
my soul
to forget/unimagine
the marcos-era phillipines
where the girlz
my age are consumed
with the approval and funding
of the u.s. government

but even here in the u.s.
my veil covers me
sometimes i imagine it
as the small mole on my chin
blackening out my existence
existence veiled by a delicate ceiling of
lace
stained by the virgin
blood of my many colored
sisters
sisters of the veil
veiled by
myself
tripping on my own
caught in a world of
sheer lace discoloring

II.
been here in the u.s.
now almost 7 years
stop saying america
cuz america don't exist
it's a fuckin' myth
fuckin' cuz it reproduces/rapes
myth cuz it hides the veil
of native- not american
but indigenous bloodshed

smell the blood
can't sleep at night
cuz the redwoods scream the stench
veiled by a chainsaw
to nourish the fuckin' myth

III.
my friend rosita
is a product of the myth

american indian

refusing to be occupied
she sits at Phil Henry's
fresh and pink
smelly like field of dandelions bubble bath
sipping a Pink Lady
through a candy-striped straw
strawberry lips
occasionally
sucking on a Winston Light
talking to the spirits about the father of her third child
rodeo star george scabbyrobe

IV.
they call me rosita cuz i used to be pretty
pretty like a rose

when i was pretty
i used to go over to Phil Henry's
and order a Pink Lady
thinking i am The Pink Lady
Lady in Pink
soft and flowery
well deserving of this
foamy and fruity drink
especially for me
rosita

V.
i am indigenous
she is immigrant
same color
mutual story
i am other
consuela says "here is rosita, my friend. she is 100%
    navajo. touch her."
she thinks that's cool
and so do i
but when she says it out loud
to a crowd
i don't think it's cool
i just feel the veil
veil of being other
the less known other

VI.
consuela can't sleep at night
she hears the screams
healers say that's the gift
but the gift is her

she is a gift
from learning how not to want
who needs to learn how to sleep

awakened each night
by scream after scream
manong sisters
screams recycled
immigrated to the u.s.

she is a gift
chosen
scaly from the veil of occupation
lying in bed each night
occupied
by her own gift

VII.
rosita tells me
i gotta know the significance of da cigarette in my
mouth cuz da spirits are listening
cuz she talks with me elevated we are at the same place
and this is her land and in whose terms i am operating
under when i say i have every right to be here cuz i
was raped where i was and she is now raped by me
twice over
this land is not my land but hers &_____
she hears those screams too
but at least she can sleep

but when we sit wherever in public wherever together
we are the same cuz the indigenous look is
recognizable as same and i am navajo and i am not cuz
i am pilipina and that means i am a mutated mass full
and empty of everybody indigenous to me and foreign
and surplus and added and she is 100 percent full
blood navajo i call her an endangered species but she
is also pilipina sometimes even to me when i see her
in me and she is me sometimes when she looks me in
the eye

of her camera thru mine cuz we both move in image
tongue tied holding each other up with the rope of the
collections of our larger images on screen she is squaw
and princess at the same time cuz that's what she's
told and i am brown open vagina cuz that's what i see
and she knows there's more to me than that and her
body is a bridge like her mouth linking into mine

VIII.
rosita's gotta gift too

she remembers thru her veins
body jagged from screaming out
over 500 years of scars

her memory is mine recycled
inside each other
puking up the myth
uncovering the veil

rosita gotta gift
her gift is me & my gift is hers

NIGHT TRAVEL
esther g. belin

I.
i like to drive to LA by myself.
my trips to the crowded   smoggy   polluted by brown
indigenous and immigrant haze   are healing.
i travel from one pollution to another.
being urban i return to where i came from
my mother
survives in LA.
now
for almost forty years.

i drive to LA in the darkness of the day
on the road before CHP
one with the dark
driving my black truck
invisible on my journey home.

the dark roads take me to my childhood.
riding in the camper of daddy's truck headed home.
my brother   sister   and i   would be put to sleep in the
    camper
and   some time   in the darkness of the day
daddy would climb into the cab with mom carrying a
    thermos full of coffee and some extra pendleton
    blankets.
and they would pray
before daddy started the truck
for journey mercies.

often i'd rise from my lullaby sleep and stare into the
    darkness of the road
the long darkness empty of cars
glowy from daddy's headlights and lonesome from
    Hank William's deep and twangy voice singing of
    cold nights and cheatin' hearts.

about an hour from flagstaff
the sun would greet us
and the harsh light would break the darkness
and we'd be hungry from travel and for being almost
    home.

II.
driving into the darkness of the day
my truck's headlights
glow the road before me.
when i drive by the fruitvale exit
headed out of oakland on my way home
i think of jamie
and i realize i will always know him.

III.
i know the darkness of the roads
endless into the glowy path before me
lit by the moon high above and the heat rising high
    from my truck's engine.
the humming from tires stays with me   mile after mile
endless along side roadside of fields shadowy from
    glow.

i know the darkness of the day
dark like my skin
and ironic like my indigenous during my time in
    berkeley.

my darkness of day
less traveled
less known.
less traveled like my path
less known like my brown
however exposed to the same pollution.
institutional smog

dark like my skin   inhaled through my lungs
    clogging my heart
ironic like my indigenous   resistant to my words
    surviving by my existence.

RUBY AWAKENS

esther g. belin

red
i find myself
sitting on a hard bench
doing quillwork
quillwork i can't believe
on a pair of jeans

what the fuck
this is useless
fuckin' A
dusty travelers pounding my head with sharp tack
    stares
bus terminal bench laughing so loud
i can't hear the time

i find myself
without memory
doing star quillwork
sitting on my bare ass
cuz the jeans are mine

what the fuck are you looking at
fuckin' A, i hate white people
a tall gothic clock with crossed eyes won't give me the
    time
chiming out of spite

red
with no memory
i slip on my jeans
star quillwork on my ass
cold marble-floor with faces
gnaw my bare feet
where's the bathroom
i ask the gothic clock and the marble-floor and i can't
    hear them cuz the travelers start pounding the tacks
    with their feet

i fuckin' hate white people

the bus terminal bathroom
fun house
with two dingy-green rows of stalls
and i can't find my way to the toilet
so i squat to pee
and the mirror in front of me
starts crawling like a panther
and the sink flash floods

what the fuck
fuckin' A, what happened
streaked red
bloodied red
i'm bruised red with swollen cheek
squatting
starring into the shiny ceramic tiled floor
looking for my memory.

RUBY AND CHILD

esther g. belin

memory is tricky
going deep into your bones
calcium sweet with nourishment
as mutton ribs on tongue
chewy in mouth
greasy like frybread

memory will kick in like last year's acid trip
when the earth sang out like the Black Lodge Singers
grand entry
calling all nations to dance
and your feet will know the song

memory is intricate
bundles of wool
sheared from sheep
dyed with roots
weaving charms of beauty way
like old growth trees
recording time.

RUBY'S SUMMER FRUIT

esther g. belin

i walk down the street
red with happiness
glowy as summer fruit
carrying a brown bag
peaches, nectarines, pears & grapefruit

walking red
curvy down the street
arms full of fruit
headed home
3-story apartment building
off fruitvale avenue near mac arthur boulevard

walking into beauty
beauty with dark hair
smiling with the morning
and me ripe with summer fruit
drop my bag
as sex gushes off my body
down the street after beauty.

RUBY'S WELFARE

esther g. belin

standing in line
after being told
indians don't stand in line
cuz a kiowa woman at window #6
helps the skins

time passes me
still in line

man at window #1
tells me welfare is a luxury
and how come i don't have a job
check the time
i smile
place my forms in the box marked
LEA VE FO R M S H ER E
black black and bold
welfare is a luxury
place your form in our box
play by our rules

i laugh
sit
smoke a Virginia Slim
and talk to the spirits

people talk about luxury
but what they mean is obligation
obligation to remain lower class
for food
$4.25 an hour
doesn't feed three

again
i check the time
light another Virginia Slim
not finished with the spirits

luxury
the u.s. forgot the definition
forgetting who allowed them to create the u.s.
through obligation of treaty
honored through
IHS and a truckload of commods
luxury overextended
obligation 500 years behind

ready to light Virginia Slim #3
i'm called by window #6

SPIRIT IN ME

esther g. belin

*WHEN I WAS YOUNG I MET THE SPIRIT AND I KNEW I
DIDN'T WANT IT BUT THE CHOICE WAS NEVER MINE
•THIS IS FOR ALL MY RELATIONS•*

i go back to the day i was driving
in the pit of the painted desert near lower greasewood
   on the navajo reservation
driving my mom's truck
not feeling anything
except the spirit
the spirit of alcohol chased me and
rode beside me and held my hand and led me to
a few days before
the day of the 6.3 earthquake in the california desert
when my mom's voice shook the house
she told me
the spirit of alcohol caught nathan and
he isn't coming back
imprisoned by his own body destroying itself
and all i could think about is how i love him and how
   we loved each other and back then it was real and it
   was good and the memory made me cry cuz i
   never wanted him dead
only healed
weaned from alcohol
and now he's dying and the parts of me i gave him are
   dying too and i cry harder cuz the parts of himself
   he gave me
the talents he never used that i use now to stay alive
   won't die when he does
and i start to drive faster cuz the spirit of alcohol is
   still walking alongside me
and i hear it talking sweet and
singing old songs and
i almost want to sing along like i know the words and
i just have to remember and

i think about this spirit
cuz i see it in me
so back when i used to drink
i never could drink miller lite
cuz that meant the spirit got you
caged
like nathan and daddy and uncle john and aunt rosita
and me too maybe
cuz i see them in me and i'm caged like them
but in a different way
cuz i can see them when they can't and
i can see the spirit scream out of them in rage and
i can love them and they can't love back
cuz the spirit took it outta them and
all i know how to do is keep loving them
believing i'm like the reservation deep and wide
nestling spirits greater than alcohol.

TRINITY

R. Dewitt

I

It was July 16th, 1945. As best as they could remember, it was Saturday because they drove their daughter to Albuquerque to see her doctor on Saturday mornings.

As they drove North, up the arid Rio Grande Valley, along the route once known as the Jornado del Muerto, the pre-dawn darkness was broken by a flash across the eastern sky, broader than the sun. The rancher and his wife still remembered their daughters words:

"What was that ?" She exclaimed.

"Was that unusual ?" An interviewer asked.

"You see," the old man said, "my daughter was born blind."

II

At Trinity Site, physicist Enrico Fermi coolly wagered with other scientists that the device, when detonated, would create a chain reaction with atoms in the atmosphere which would result in a fireball 500 miles wide.

III

> ...As West and East
> In a flatt Maps---and I am one---are one,
> So death doth touch the Resurrection.
> -JOHN DONNE

IV

The SANTA FE NEW MEXICAN reported in a two inch
story on page 6 of its August 6, 1945 edition:
MAGAZINE LETS GO AT ALAMOGORDO.

V

We have sought the face of gods with our minds,
and that god is fire.

SHADOW OF THE GODS

Elias Funaro

Look up to the night sky my friend, tell me what you
    see
The blackness that surrounds the earth in a blazing
    star filled sea

Where questions pend our human souls and plagues
    our wonderous minds
Endless journeys with no beginnings, Imaginations
    running blind

Where 1000 stars are laying, Sleeping in their
    darkened bed
Where religion gets its reason for the kingdom of the
    dead

Where the thunderous silence echoes and plays a
    quiet song
While the galaxies are laying in the Giant Nothing's
    palm

The Gods in shadows watching from the obscure void
as we rage pathetic anarchy in a world so paranoid

we know not of the reasons for the big black sea above
While the end lies over the edge and we still continue
    to shove

This universal space, the subconscious travels far
Look up to the night sky my friend, remember how
    small we are

MANGO MAN

Sorrel Goodwin

Mango Man
Wheelin
Kings Road
Kingston vibration
Fruit cart in the Caribbean
Fire
Aged....Lion Locks
having seen many Diaspora
years
educated
Biblically
(African Bible)
cornhusk sculpted
cannabis sacrament
Lit in a flash of
Dread
Instant visions
Jamaican winter
wheeling
Hope Road
Mango Man
smilin
Caribbean sunset
Pum! Pum!
Gunshots
Shantytown
Again
Yankee tourists
Sand? Sun?
Bloodclot.
Mango Man
glarin

Blue Mountain Bound
home
Mango Man Home

BUCKET OF CRABS

Sorrel Goodwin

Bucket of crabs
One
Crab
Climbing
Striving
to reach
the top
of
the oaken bucket
Illusionary
success
One crab's   peers (brothers?)
sneering
striving   planning
plans   on top of
plans
to pull
One Crab's success
down
down
DOWN
into   the bottom of the
Bucket

RAVEN MY BROTHER

Sorrel Goodwin

Raven   My Brother
Ebony Trickster
Bringer of
Sun   Moon   Stars
caw! caw!
YEIL   MY BROTHER
Sculptor   to my people
Tlinglit
out of Beach grass
fashioned
He
us
caw! caw!
Raven   My Brother
Water Bearer
instructor
Light
to fish by
allowing
salmon feast
in June
Gaa!   Gaa!

UNTITLED

Sorrel Goodwin

Sun Kissed
Messiah
standing with judgment
yet
disrespected by
United?
Nations?
fascist   warning
ignored
Second   world
WAR
inevitable
Lion of
Judah
standing   with judgment
Jihad   Holy?War?
mental
loyalty
Abrams   sons
crash   dummies
for   A
big big big big BIG BIG BIG
picture
Lily of the valley
Addis Ababa
standing with judgment

MICHAEL LUJAN

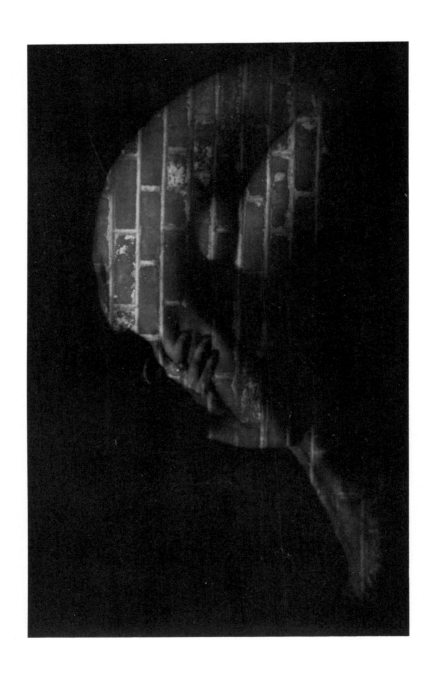

MAJA MUNK

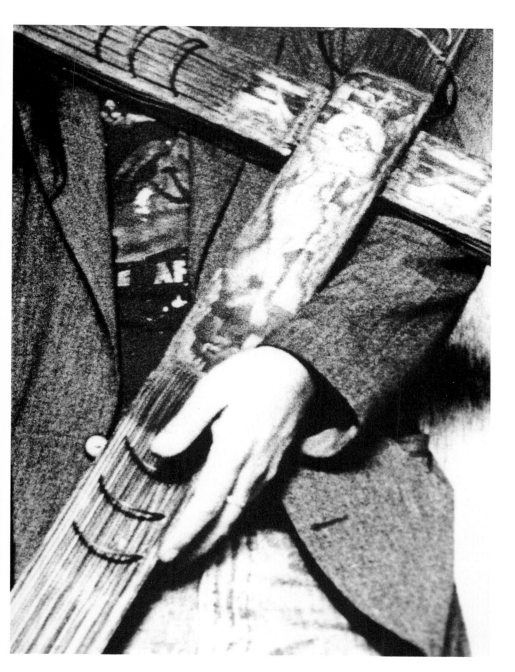

MICHAEL LUJAN

MARWIN BEGAYE

CHARLES SHEPPARD

MICHAEL LUJAN

MICHAEL CYWINK

MARWIN BEGAYE

PICO & 20TH

Sorrel Goodwin

The Big Blue bus
Deisel Defication
over
a fungus yellow sky?
Whopper   No Ketchup
Dining with crips
Burger King   Rock
stars
Fuck Flik   Dailys
50c
Pick and choose   your
crackhead
vixen
within
The city of no angels
Pico & 20th
The American Dream
Bitch

MT. ZION IN ROME?

Sorrel Goodwin

Fire for the Pope!
Roman
Taskmaster
Spreading the disease
false profit (Prophet?)
up to his Robe in
BLOOD
wringing it
out
with no luck
Fire for the Pope!
POP LEO XI
INTOXICATED
While Drinking
Cocaine
Vino
While Deceiving
Zombiotic
Masses
eating themselves
changing
Sabbath
to
Sunday while
Hallucinating
Cocaine apparitions of
White washed
Jesus
KILL POPE PAUL
BABYLON FALL
Fire for the Pope!

AN IYESKA'S WAR
Arthur John Harvey

George felt the fear as it crept up on him. It always seemed to start this way, the calculated quiet, just before the rush. For George and the two other soldiers their orders were clear. Observe the enemy, assassinate as many Chinese officers as possible, and report battle positions. Being a forward observer was George's sole priority, and although he had already registered four kills, the idea of looking down the barrel of your rifle and killing another human being still churned his stomach.

The first flares lit up the night sky. George immediately began scanning with his binoculars, while reading out the coordinates, as the other two began relaying them back to the big guns. Enhanced by the white snow on the ground, the sky became brilliantly lit. Everything was clearly visible. The first explosions were deathly close and the ground seemed to come alive. George began wondering if this old Korean bunker would hold out. He and the other soldiers scrunched down and held onto their helmets, as each blast trembled the earth. A sudden thought filled George's head. There aren't any atheists in foxholes, and for him, this was the absolute truth. When the action started there was nothing to do but hug good old mother earth and pray. It was amazing how close he had become with the dirt since he had joined the Army. As of late, kissing the ground had become his pastime.

The shelling stopped as suddenly as it began and although the temperature was well below freezing, he noticed he was sweating profusely. This was the moment he hated. The sheer terror. He had seen it before, but the first wave never seemed to amaze him. He always thought of them as ants. A human wave hundreds of yards wide, and perhaps as thick. It was a magnificent, and yet horrifying spectacle.

The machine-guns behind began firing and the bodies started to fall. These were the moments when George wished he could be back home.

Thinking back to the beginning, he hadn't realized that it would turn out like this. He remembered the first time he had tried to join the Marines. He was only nineteen years old and the Pine Ridge Reservation held no future for him. He hitchhiked to the nearest recruiting station, which was located in Rapid City, South Dakota, only to be told by a mean looking leatherneck that he needed a high-school education. He later joked with his family.

"I must have looked pretty pitiful, because the Marine recruiter softened a little and told me, 'Try the Army, it's just a few blocks that a way.'
" I tell you, I was played out, and to make matters worse, the war broke out while I was still in boot camp." Those days were gone and war was a cold reality.

Born and raised in the Badlands of South Dakota, George had enjoyed a happy childhood. Although, life was hard for most people on the reservation, his family never seemed to have it too bad. His Grandpa, who he was named after, had come from the east and George was always fascinated with this man who seemed so secretive. He was a quiet and stern man, who George was always leery of. The only son of an English immigrant, he had struck out on his own after the death of his parents. After roaming about for a few years, he met and married a Oglala Sioux woman named Molly Iron Teeth. From this union, George's father John, and his three uncles were born. They were allotted land, under the Indian Allotment Act, by the Cuny Table in the Badlands of South Dakota. There they began raising cattle and horses for the U.S Cavalry, who were stationed in Rapid City, South Dakota, at the time. This double standard never occurred to George, until his later years. A white man married to a full-blooded Sioux, selling horses to the U.S. cavalry, right after all the battles between the Indians and the Government. George never questioned anything. These things never really occurred to him, or bothered him. He was just happy to have all the comforts of a big family. His early years were filled with memories of riding horses and fishing the White River for catfish. His father John, the eldest in the family, was a half-breed who spoke fluent English as well as Sioux. He married a half-breed by the name of Mary, George's mother, who instilled the Lakota values in him. George had a brother and a sister,and they were all raised in a bilingual household. They never moved from the original homestead, which was located just a few miles from the main house.

He never had to do very much around the place; his father and uncles took care of everything. The only time he had to do any work was when they halter broke the horses, or harvested the garden. Back then all the neighboring families raised huge gardens, including his own. He can remember him and his brother stealing watermelon in the moonlight from other people's gardens, even though they grew their own, or throwing bullets in a campfire for fireworks, because they didn't have any for the fourth of July. He recalled trapping and hunting in the winter and listening to the Lakota stories his Grandma, and mom, told by the light of the woodstove. After the death of his Grandparents, things began to get hard. Their large herd of horses dwindled when the cavalry advanced to modern technology. Then World War II hit and the Air Force confiscated most of the land in that area, converting it into a bombing range. A lot of families lost their land, including George's. His father had to turn the majority of their horses loose, because they had to leave immediately. They were given a little relocation money, but not anything compared to what they used to have. These were the hectic times in George's life. From a comfortable life in the country, to being forced to live deep inside the reservation. This is where George began to realize that he didn't fit in. The Indian kids began calling him "iyeska sica." When he asked his mother why they called him that, she used to tell him, " Never mind them, they don't know what they are saying."

This answer didn't cut it and he started asking his father questions. After this he became more aware of his background. He just didn't seem to fit in anywhere. If it wasn't the Indians calling him down, it was the white farmers he worked for making fun of Indians in front of him and calling him chief. The reservation wasn't for him, and he decided to get away.

George thought the Army was the answer, so he joined up. After bootcamp, where he was still called chief, he was shipped to Camp Chaffee, Arkansas, where he received his training. From there, he was shipped directly overseas. When told he would be a forward observer, he had no idea that his marksmanship would come into play. His trip overseas was terrible. He got seasick, and loneliness began to set in.

When they arrived in southern Korea, the troops he was with began to become excited with the talk of upcoming action. The sight of the little Korean kids begging for food hurt George. They reminded him of the Indian children back home and he wondered how these homeless kids would ever survive this. The cold was terrible and some of these children were practically naked. He offered a young child a candy bar from his K- rations, when this guy next to him said, " Don't give that gook anything. Don't you know some of these kids are killing American soldiers with grenades strapped to their bodies?"

George couldn't believe it and gave the kid the candy bar anyway. The other soldier gave him a look of disgust.

"You got a lot to learn chief, over here, a gook's a gook."

That was then and now he didn't know what to think. The first detail he was assigned was stringing up wire for communications. He wasn't up front, so he wasn't too worried, although the danger of shelling was ever present. After about a month he heard rumors (scuttlebutt it was called) that his company was due to move up to the front lines. He didn't actually believe it, but within a week they were moving out. The first two nights out were pretty quiet, but the next day a detail went out and when they came back there was plenty of excitement. They had run into a small group of north Koreans and pretty well wiped them out. When George heard all the commotion, he ran outside the tent and saw a soldier carrying around a gook's head stuck on a bayonet. From then on out, George knew he was in a war.

The thunder of the shelling, and the steady pop of the machine-guns was deafening, but even with this noise he couldn't shut out the shouts and the screams of men dying. It was totally insane. Why did they keep coming? How could they keep coming,in a never ending flow. The guns were getting hot, starting to jam, and on they came. To George it was apparent they were going to be overrun. There was nothing they could do. The Chinese were willing to sacrifice men to gain ground and with the advantage of manpower they were going to do it. The enemy was too close for George and his men to retreat. Their only hope was to secure the hatches and ride it out. Hopefully their troops would make a push, retaking the area. The shouts of the men were getting louder, as the ground began to slightly rumble. George was reminded of the stories his grandmother used to tell, about how the buffalo would make the ground shake when they stampeded. Now all the buffalo were gone, all the good old days are gone, and here he sat wondering if he was ever going to see his family again.

The first thing he saw was total whiteness, his head felt like it was going to explode. Needles in his eyes. *Make the pain go away, pull out the needles and he would be O.K.* His thoughts were incoherent. *Was he alive?* George tried to open his eyes again; this time the pain was less severe. He thought he could make out images. After squeezing his eyes shut, then tentatively opening them to a slit a few times, he was able to see a little. It was apparent he was in a bed, but where he didn't know. *How long had he been here? Where were his friends?* Most of all, he thought, *Where in the hell was he?*

After a few minutes of adjusting to the light, he was able to see better. He realized he was in a hospital. He could tell by the rows of beds to the right and left of him and directly across. Some of the people in the beds were immobile, while others were sitting up reading or talking. It seemed strange that he just now realized he could hear. There was the chatter of people talking and the echo of laughter down the hall. Little by little thoughts came back to him and he now realized that he was truly alive. He had survived and now he would be going home. Back home to the family and country that was so much a part of him.

SPORTING WITH BEN

Arthur John Harvey   *to Conroy*

I'm carrying a rusty load
Shouting curses
In snowy moonlight
Me and Ben
Puffing on mavericks
swilling cheap beer
Hawking old haunts
"See that Camaro"
"Shall we give it a test"
Looks like a shiny beer can
Crushed a little
In the front
Bruce is singing
"Born in the U.S.A."
Spark that "J"
So I can see
Those blood shot eyes
As you lean back
In your ripped up seat
A white
Bad ass demon
Is what you drive
Catch us if you can

BACKROADS

Arthur John Harvey

It's the weather
Stirs a wild hair
Low grey clouds
Cold crisp air
I want
To take a shot
Old crow whiskey
Don't laugh angry
Feel blue madly
With my buddies
Drive around
In a car
That smells
Like stale beer
Old cigarette
Butts
Listen
To Damn good jams
Over the FM stereo
Taking a leak
In the glow
Of red taillights
Forgetting your beer
Until it falls
Clunking
spraying
As you spin Gravel
Down the road

LAKOTA WARRIOR

Arthur J. Harvey   *for my father*

My Lakota father
War hero
Drafted at 21
Thrust into obliviance
Regimented   trained
Small   skinny
In crisp army green
Always smiling   fresh
Tentatively
Remembrance
Of drunken rage
Crying
For people
Slain
Korean children
Spookily familiar
Like   ones
Left at home

Heat of war
Extreme cold

Slivers in legs
Unconscious memories
"hit the deck"
My brothers are dead
Useless medals
Army suit
Burned
Silver medal
Bronze medal
Lost
Lost blackness
Six months
He did not complain
Only saluted
At moment of death.

108

DECEMBER

Arthur J. Harvey   *For Unc*

Uncle Wilbert
Killed two deer
As I watched
In awe

He circled them
Twice
Knelt and slit
The stomach open

Curdly steaming guts
Tumbled to the ground
I turned
Almost heaved

He laughed
"Hokshila,
Are you
Winkte"

Standing
Gory Knife
In rough hand
"humph

Help me
You won't glepa
When your mother
Fries the meat"

HOLDOUT

Arthur John Harvey

Soft white
flakes

Of gentle snow
Float slowly down
To settle upon
Already blanketed ground

This rolling flat land
I love so much
Is so alone
Peaceful
I am alone except
For my prayers

I see
The fort's
Smoke
Adrift in distance
Over horizon
My people there
Safe

I am the last
I refuse to fold
Starving and yet
My heart
Too sick to eat
I am cold
But   my boiling anger
Warms me inside

The air is
Still
I can almost hear

Snow sizzle
As it melts
On
My brown skin
My horse senses
He hangs his head
Refuses to graze
I cannot make fire
He's   my only warmth

Soldiers
Sniff
And plunder
Through   snow
In search   of me
They do not know
That this land   is part
Of me
And I   it

Sometimes
When   nights are
Mine
I sit atop   a barren hill
Crisp white stars
Only companions
Breathing crystal   white
Watching   tohansis and kolas
As they   transform
Before   my dreary eyes
But   the uncis and takojas
Are not osni   or hungry

Still
Chest heaves
It is finished

My anger   hate
Turned
Into sorrow

I   like a lone
Starving wolf
Caught
In Wasicu's
Steeljawed trap
Chewing my own leg
Off
Crawl away
To die
Free

HARDCORE
Arthur John Harvey

Chronic cheek kiss
Affecting   halfbreed
Master   playing catch-up
Soothing seared egos
Strategic games
Careful placement
Wooden Indian
Porcelain china
Chesspieces

Confrontation
On
Charming
greenback
Snake scales
Ruling
Devising
Petty rewards   A wards
While
Hardcore skins
Remain
Hard

BREEDS

Arthur J. Harvey

Such a mockery
Long hair   blue eyes
Indian   and white
Is this   what they
Had in mind?
Those that fought for our land
Who did the slaughtering
Aggressive
Passive
A nation turned tail
Can you imagine
Custer
CrazyHorse
Friends

P.O.W.'S/INDIAN WARS

Arthur John Harvey

They locked me in shackles
Broke both wrists
And shaved my head bald
Did I break
Did I succumb
To their desires
And sign that filthy sheet

LITTLE, KHLETES

Arthur John Harvey   *for Marcus and Jay Dee*

Little blackfeet
Running through the ashes
Fast as a waterbug
Can't catch me
You'll starve to death first
Then
I will bang you, in the head
With a burnt pot
Giggling as I laugh with dread

STRETCH
Arthur J. Harvey

Blue eagle
Flies higher and high
Circling the sun
Singeing his wing tips

Glossy red
Marble eyes
Screams of doom
Float
Arrow straight down

Burning my ears
Searing my throat
As I stare
At the halo of flame

PRETTY LITTLE MISS PANSY

Arthur John Harvey

The brass is blue
So piss on the gold
Until my spirit is broke
laugh at my legs
cry to my dad
cut a hole in my heart
let me laugh, until I scream
I will devour your mind
Hopscotch with William
Play jacks with Jill
Cuss at the holes in the wall
Look at the flag
Is that red
Or the blood of a breed
Who's bawling wet white
Because he's blue
Such a joke
Your thoughts and mine
Intermingled
We think we're cool

BLACKNESS

Arthur John Harvey

In search of a dream
I kissed a fly
Caught in a black widows web
And was
Entangled myself
Try as I may
I slowly grew numb
Until
I was
Pinched into new
Thoughts
Of triangular patterns
Pressed into
Silky wetness
And lavender black
Trapped inside
A cotton
Safe
Controlled
Cocoon

THE MOST

Arthur John Harvey

for my mother

There she sits
Huggable   sweet
Cheeks aglow
Her eye
Sparkle
Talking of us with pride
She's had
A tough life
Tougher than most
She is a survivor
She is bold
Ask me   who is the best cook
When I'm alone   where do I go
If I'm sick   who comforts me
Who tells each of us
"I love you the most"
 Thinks we don't know
 She is a Grandma
Her kids   grown
She wonders   will she be alone
She need not worry
Her tokajas are many
Her house will never be cold
Sometimes when I
Am alone
With waves of blue
I think of her
Suddenly
My life has meaning
Like hearing
Her assure me
Everything will be fine
"my son"

YOUNG BLOOD

Arthur John Harvey   *for Stevie*

Zhe, Zhe
Little head
Small striped T shirt
Tiny rank one
Chest thrust out
"Ardle" he says
Young glow
Sparkling eyes
"I'm a beat you up"
Wrestling on the couch
Chubby cheeks
Red
He has a fire
Growing inside

SWEETNESS

Arthur John Harvey   *for my niece*

Tiny butterfly
China doll strength
Streaming hair of wind
An untouched snowflake

Irritating giggle
Bushy
Muddy knees
Playing cars
Patting mudcakes
Wrestling with the boys

Reading
The grocery list
For Grandma
Skipping to the store
A sprouting beauty
I call her
"Genie"

GROWING PATTERNS
Arthur John Harvey   *for AHC*

Did I tell you, that I need you
In my silent dream
While you lay sweating
Thinking of me
If you really hold me
It will begin to show
Because you   are like a lion
Draped in velvet and cream

Yesterday, I heard your voice
While thinking out loud
When all it was   was
Whispers of fantasies
memories of night
Playful   while I was mean
Keep touching me
Make me believe   it's real

Each day we grow stronger
Our bodies more conformed
I began to feel
when I am alone
That you were born   and live
Match perfect for me

RESPONSES

A. A. Hedge Coke

skin light, tinged yellow-olive
sharp ridge bone top cheeks
tassel strands spinning gold, gold,
scalloped backs of frontal teeth
laced tennis shoes outside
wrapped feet turned forever in
integrated world
sovereign traditional culture
dominant language
indigenous language
forget the past
you are the past
one and the same
specific result
of   interracial marriage
product parcel
of   modern man
one strangles
one survives
I am a survivor
I know who I am
myself, I know
you ask outright
"Were you raised by Indians?"
"How do you know those songs?"
"How can this be?"
I confuse you   and
in your confusion
you demand
far past my visual perceptions
through me   not   at me
past me   not   here
where I am
"There must be   some

mistake." you say
I politely and not so politely
inform you
that this is what happens
when you snag a skin
for experimental purposes
for the *Native American Experience*
and your own flesh and blood offspring
cannot survive in your world
the world you manifested for yourself
your own child belongs
to another world, another way,
and you may never come into
that world no matter how
hard you coerce
it is a simple matter of blood
and culture conveniently deny
you have your own
you must be ashamed, I guess, by now
but you cannot fix it
by stealing more of mine
it's just not for sale
it never really was
nor will it ever be
you marvel at my poetry techniques
and how on earth this
breed woman-child
can take a simple menu
and read:

Famous Burger
Greek Salad
French Fries

Toasted American Cheese Sandwich
Fish on a Bun
Top Sirloin Butt Steak
Chicken Parmesan
Breaded Veal Dinner
Chop Sirloin
Flounder Dinner
Shakes

can take your trash
and furnish a life
can take so much   and
dare explode on select occasion
and yet   you   take and take and take
and want more
you   who created
my   people's struggle
and my own personal interracial existence
some of your very own people   sometimes
treat me as a human being
not as an oddity, a curio,
not expecting me to pass
--as if I would ever even want to be you--
but   to accept that I am   different
and they are few
and I am many
we are the mixed-bloods
the war babies
and conceptions of more humanistic humans
or so we ..ould like   to believe
and intend to
the breeds   and even those

far removed metis and mestizo
who would like to forget both
sides of themselves
and create a new "modern" version of culture
but I, myself, I refuse to accept
less than the utmost
satisfaction in surviving
in your wannabee world
no matter what the cost
rather than sell out
exploit, forget, pass off...
if you miss me
you missed the boat
maybe on the way to America
land of the free
for some
for your great white hope
not for me
or maybe on your way to
Indian Country
to snag your own personal skin
I know for you it's all smoke
in your blindness   don't ever
confuse white with red
you might miss the boat

LEGACY   from Anthology O   *(dual voice performance)*

A. A. Hedge Coke *for Chris Apache; Chris, Mike, &*
Lisa Brooks;   Art Harvey; and James Luna

in 1992

Surviving in the post
traumatic era in
the dark ages following
the systematic genocidal
encroachment of the
displaced invaders,
intruders, currently
occupying
and implementing martial
law
throughout the western
hemisphere

All you eastern hemisphere
people   are   just alike
You expect us   to believe
Europe and Asia   are   NO ADC
separate continents
and that we walked across   NO BIA
from over there
or   that   space   NO CIB
invaders built our
pyramids and
medicine wheels   NO SERVICE
for us--R. L. Hedge Coke

Good thing we had
fish on hand
you might have
starved--R. L. Hedge Coke

128

So, your ancestors
were fresh off the
boat, huhn, the
Mayflower, huhn,
mine were here to meet them

Smallpox, measles, typhoid,
T.B., syphilis--all of
these   we acquired
in exchange for
a pair of glasses--   Booze, alcohol   the
        Dehl Berti   s l o w smallpox blanket
                                we are still trying
                                to uncover its
                                disastrous effects

Hudson Bay Blankets
    &
Hudson Bay Rum
                                Ban the Booze   in
                                Indian Country
                                Abolish the s l o w trade
                                blanket

                        That old man   you called a
                        drunk,   dirty,   Indian
                        is my father.   He never did take
                        the drink you poured down my
                        throat.   Your manager said he
                        could get these boxes in the
                        alley   to pack some   things in
                        that we are moving. That man
                        has a   college education.
                        He grew up in a dug out,   in the
                                1920's.

He fought with honors in your
World War II.
He went to medical school
 riding fence   to pay in
Grand Forks   before there
was an InMED.
He worked for your Agriculture
Department,   for your
 Helium Research, for your
NASA,   for the E.P.A.   until
you gave him
bronze medals and claimed we
 no longer needed environmental
protection.   That man knows
our old ways   and your new
ways   that you   yourself
are too slow and stupid to
grasp.   You'd better watch who
you call   dirty and drunk   that's
my father.   He bathed in rivers
while   you   powdered yourself
   to   hide your   smell.

It's a computer pow wow
Japanese Apple Mac   Intosh
Hey, What's that?
Hey, come check this out.
What is that?
Hey, this pow wow's
points   are added up
on a lap top computer.
Looks like a toy.
Hey, get over here.
Dancers be on the floor

at 1:30 Mac Intosh
Time. No, not Indian Time.
Japanese computer time.
Grand Entry at 1:30
MacIntosh Pow Wow Time.
Institute for American Indian Arts
Thirtieth Anniversary   1962--1992
Spring Celebration Pow Wow
I hear that the Writing Majors
protested for these computers
It's about time   we got hold of
some choice equipment.

we used to say
don't spin webs
the white man says
don't spin wheels
we turn that around
and say   to our
young
spin creations

every ridge
a bone
every peak
a vertebra
rising,
forming
your skeleton
following
every
mound and
crevasse
I see
your spirit
living
standing upon
your skin
I feel
my spirit
living, too

That Dine'
man
he   stumbled blinded
right across   the
Santa Fe Rail
looking   for the
curb shop
in Gallup.
That white man shot him
said he thought   he
was a   deer.

                    I am a young woman
                    I respect my elders
                    I follow my heart
                    and   use my mind to
                    benefit my community.
                    I am a single mother.
                    I respect my children.
                    I nurture their talents
                    and encourage them to
                    use their minds
                    to benefit their community

Our mother is crying
Our grandfather
he looks at us
and he cries, too   The principals we   were
                            raised with
                        in a good way, as females, as
                            Indians,
                        generosity; empathy;
                            compassion;
                        loyalty...
                                Today
                        due to the momentous

change inflicted upon us
by the European transplant
society
marks us   like   targets
to be used, cruised, abused
conned and taken
   advantage of
even by   some of our
own   people
Continue on
on the other side
your walk
will be remembered
honored, respected.
Even   when   the
endurance
is all winter   after   winter
all that really matters
is that you help
someone   somewhere
along your   path
grow
Physically, mentally,
emotionally, or spiritually,
even by laying
a hand on the shoulder
of a crying   stranger
and praying in   your
mind
You can help
by
turning   tears
to   smiles   and

A warrior helps an old person,
a child, a single woman.
A warrior is not someone
with braids, sunglasses
and a cool statement--
     Bull Bear

133

Phil Sheridan   was
the hard enemy
he put the bounty
on the buffalo
Custer was nothing
but a rapist and baby killer--
R. L. Hedge Coke

You better be careful
if you say the truth
the Feds will have
to kill you

I wish I never told you
as much as I did
now you're a threat

you know too much

Defend your people
Defend our way of life

laughter
if   the time
is right
grow
and help others
grow
and your tears
can also
turn to
smiles
and laughter
rather than
falling rain
from the old
ones   crying
above
continue on

They told us that
this generation
would
eat our children
What they meant
was that our men
would take our ADC
and drink it up and
use it
for gas and leave
us and our kids
hungry and
without

Be willing to give your life
to do these things

One hundred thousand
American   Indians
reside in Los Angeles and
greater   L.A.   No greater
concentration   in an urban
community may be
found in the United States, even
almost as large as the population
on the Dine' reservation,
   Navajos.
I went into the PHS in
Ventura County   just next
door to L.A. and   there was
no box that said American
   Indian
or Native American   on the
   form.   Once
again I checked off OTHER,
once again I got angry,
once again   I understood,
   this is our land, our
   health care

For them only   We are yet OTHER
They say it means   only to you   and
justice   just-us--   your voice of justice
   F.J. Thunder Hawk   The only forms I found
with a box   that identified
Native peoples   were
in Indian organization
offices,   where there
were no   other   choices

other than to modify
descriptives.
When   there is   no
alternative,
no choice,
modification   only is
offered, only
modification
No solution
No   resolution

Breaking waves
Thundering brain waves
pound in cranial capacities
and migraine me   back
   home.

If   they truly respected
Crazy Horse   they would
simply name a mountain
for him and leave the
physical form   pure
rather than blasting
it into a replica
supposedly of him,
he who had no picture ever
taken,
duplicating their idea of the
concepts he stood
for   and   gave his life
to   protect   from
exploitation.

in 1492

NO, I AM NOT A VET

A.A. Hedge Coke   *for Charmaine*

Closing, closing long, still,
desperately   trying to rest
my eyes   my visionary
statement   rise
there arises   times
clips, flicks, changes
in time   slipping
back   in time   back
flash   film effect
strobe   I see
I remember white
men   white, white
men killing women   and
children   killing Indians
and men Indian men
trying desperately   to
kill me   our own
men   reacting reaction
action to oppressed
oppression repetitive
it   throws back my
face   my heart   slides
down and forth up my
bladed back and crawls
up scratched   parched
listless tongue screaming
so silently immense silence
quickening relapse tendencies
"But I didn't do anything."
and they proceed to
maim   killing thousands
hundreds, and turn
back on   one   the survivors
this precise second   in

replay   evolves repeating
dream   flash back   back
flash crashing blows   to
the frontal plane
guard my 3-D existence
terrorizing women and children
bayonets slicing   into
tiny warm bodies
beaded flags on
sacred heads   and wisdom
all ages   in their beautiful
black eyes   turning over
and back   in regard   to
overwhelming constant
batter and mix whip
lash   to certain refrain
feel the dangling
effect of rabbit punch
to rubber   punching bag
my head   my point of
conceptual   conception
thought process shield
and emergence place
I feel you reaching
through   aiming not
at me but deeper
through -- behind me
to the wall you
collide   your jabs and
hooks into my skull
protruding damage
through   object resting
above my bladed back
neck snap cheekbone
thrash   eyes no longer

have clean form but
swell beyond recognition
senseless I am suspended
yet standing   out cold
yet balanced on locked
knees   as you   pursue   your
reaction action   to the oppression
bestowed upon us
as a people   your anger
and confusion   at images
infants and women
our grandparents   and theirs
being mutilated   and so
you mutilate the mother
of your children
the grandmother of your grandchildren
and drop the bomb -- oppression
upon her   that is

was me   breaking parts
spirit   breaking my
spirit irreparably for
as long as I exist

remember

LANES

A. A. Hedge Coke   *for Art, Ruth, Travis and Vaughan*

lunar transparency   rising   through   crisp
cobalt   blue mountains
further upward into still blue   skies   still
containing   solar adversary
shrouding wind glass   appearance   opaque
where the wiper   used to cruise   until
it flew from   base   during tropical rain   in
a not so very tropical place   on the plains
the other side clean in   l o n g bow pathway
the blade yet strong   though singular
this pattern   so, so, typical   for hot, dusty, days
though it is winter   and   a hard, bitter, one at that
the road salt and slush mud collected   upon
this vehicle's face   and   splattered
upon its side   the moon gives to climbing   rise   in
    light of day
suddenly traffic halts   logic and reason creep
toward
the passengers sudden,   more sudden,   realization
no day dream   drifting   daze   only the
maze   of many, many,   more   shuttling
to work and home again   from the never ending
flow
duty and logic,   responsibility and reason,   we
know
but   try our best to   not belong,   or buy into
keeping rather   the flow   day   dreaming
scattered mental wanderings   allowing freedom
and   contentment
to run their course   across these roads
driven hurriedly, driving forces   economy and
bread
restless,   so, so, restless,   pumping, beating,
breathing physical   segments refuse
to agree whole   heartedly   and keep us in
tolerance often   without complete patience
the ambulance finally crosses   on the other side

divided highway
we realize someone's pain and situation   directly
 caused perhaps by this
relentless river   rushing cars one by tens,
hundreds   by thousands
they creep and rush toward goals delivered directly
through completion   manifest destiny
this place we witness attaining statehood   81
years   ago   today
in perilous waters we tread   they led the   march
with "don't tread on me"   and   "these savages are
not   people"
civil, civilized, civilization,   coming forth,   rising
 through
the salt,   road salt,   as the moon rising on the day
something so accepted   yet somehow   so misplaced
 balance
swings   precariously   toward   lower level scales
the oil   pours through   Shetland Seas
those islands   likened to ponies   and sheepdogs
 and lush green   rolling hills
Valdez a drop   in the   bucket   to this   day   the DJ
 warns us of the
accident and   the spill   all in one breath   the sun
 sinks

NIGHTMARE

A. A. Hedge Coke   *for Charmaine*

Like a hungry panther along the lake ridge at
Oconoluftee, he is following every breath and every
movement I make.   I can feel the weight of his eyes
pushing down on my shoulders, pinning me,
forcing me up against the rocks, and the violence
begins, like an urban riot unleashed on one small
woman.

The initial blow knocks the force of life from me
and I am defenseless--like jell-o. My head is like a
punching bag suspended in a gym. The battery of
blows continues until I can't feel my face anymore,
then the jabs and punches land in my ribs. The
blood running out my ears and nose is almost
soothing.

I hear his voice somewhere in a distance and
jerk myself awake by myoclonic spasm--my dad
taught me to wake myself up from nightmares this
way when I was about three or four years old.
Remember, the dreams you're falling in and you
land and wake at the same time and the bed is
shaking? It's like that.   When I wake I am soaked
with sweat, goosebumps form rows all over my skin.
I make myself move, turning to sit up. The
quivering slows, my teeth stop chattering and I
breathe in deeply, rhythmically. I get up and walk
around the house checking locks and latches on
doors and windows, then I splash some cool water on
my face to snap me out of the dream.

My kids are crying, afraid of me screaming in
my sleep. They've been up for hours, as usual, but
it's so hard for me to sleep at night I wait for light to
come to rest easier, sometimes. Usually, by the time
I do, I'm caught in nightmares until I force myself
awake. Poor things, probably hungry, too. Always
my ex--my kid's dad. That is the worst feeling when

142

one of your own people tries to kill you on a daily
basis; my own tribe, one of my own people, he even
has more blood than me--almost full.

Twelve years ago he was a very good-looking
man. Long, dark hair and dark brown eyes--
haunting. No one told me he was on parole, or that
he beats women. I knew he drank, but I was
just a young kid then and I drank my share, too. No
one said he was sick and cruel. As a man he came to
me in disguise--all smiles, all laughter. All of the
girls wanted him, and he wanted me. When the
laughter went away, the maniac emerged. The man
was vicious, psychopathic.

It has been behind me for a long time--nine
years--and that much time has passed since I laid
eyes on him. He said he would never bother me
again, but he lives on still, inside this realm of sleep
in my mind. Every time I think I might try life
again, he comes in dreams--haunting me. Every
time I think I am over my past, something triggers
him and calls him back.

I tried to visit my family last winter. They were
living in a one-bedroom trailer house. We used to
have one just like it when *we* were married. I was
trying to visit with my dad and I felt like I was in a
tin coffin. I flashed back to lying on the floor, face
down, with a five-month old baby under me to
protect him from flying bullets. That tiny of an
infant and his dad at war with somebody, probably a
neighbor, maybe a stranger. I got claustrophobic
and paced all night. I drove my family nuts
jumping out of bed and running through the trailer
looking out windows throughout the night, not
completely conscious--on automatic pilot--half
asleep, still dreaming.

I have been in severe depression for twelve
weeks this time, no explanation. I think about a
man I was with who really cared for me and left

here...I want to be over there with him...I feel incredibly tired. There is much sadness around us all the time, the beauty is lost in it, over *there* it is good.

I relive the guns held on me and knives, the beatings, the wrecks, the broken bones and spirit, the ruptured organs--all night sometimes. I don't want to lie down to face it again.

My dad is a World War II vet. He tells me that the Indians were all scouts or radio men over there; he was both. The Philippines, Solomons, New Guinea-- the army never gave him any of the medals or decorations he won. I have seen the discharge papers with the awards list. He said that they just stuck him on a bus to the nearest town and cut him loose. I wrote to the V.A. in 1989. He finally got six of the medals and some of the ribbons in 1990--almost fifty years late.

He looks at me like he is looking through me. He says he knows what bothers me in the night. He knew it himself after he came back from the war. He says hand to hand jungle warfare were the best and worst days of his life. The best because he felt the warrior in him (a part of our society that has been taken away leaving the men feeling that they lack something they often try to replace in military service), the worst because of the death and destruction of life.

He tells me when you live through severe violence on a day-in, day-out basis--when you are held hostage--trying to survive each hour of each day, the violence can come back again, over and over. He tells me the Vietnam vets are calling it post-traumatic stress syndrome, today. He says war is war, no matter which home front it takes place on. He tells me to recognize it and to pray about it--to face it and face the dream.

I turn on KILI Radio--Lakota airwaves, 100,000 watts strong--and I listen to the D.J. talk with a

144

white doctor from Pine Ridge, IHS, about the Indian
suicide rate and its rise in the winter, how it
increases with the cold. I wonder how many people
relive their days of terror, how many pasts haunt
today. How many vets, how many abused women and
children, all lying awake at night.

I open a can of commod meat and fix my kids
some lunch.

CALLING BLUES

A. A. Hedge Coke   *for Derya and Stephanie*

I found quiet by climbing into the warmth, the
safe place where I curled into a ball and became the
warmth myself.   I pulled the dryer's door shut after
me and silence began filling my ears with soothing
lack of sound. The desolate survivors of the outside
world locked away from my senses. I lay still and
closed my eyelids to rest. Relief, achieved at long
last, I had waited long enough for sanctuary.
Waiting until the spinning ceased and cool down
occurred but where the Maytag dryer heat was still
very intense and satisfying.
     I had watched patiently, virtually invisible,
while the customers dried their clothes, then folded
them onto tables, or into baskets, or hung them on
rods above carts. Then I stood silently, waiting
again until they departed into the rain filled streets,
into the dark. At the time the dryer cooled down
enough to tolerate its touch, I spread my blanket
inside and entered the cocoon of individual world.
Safe. Warm. Real. After spending plenty of time
basking in the security and relaxation, I emerged.
Rolling the blanket into a tight cylinder to maintain
the level of warmth, I ventured out into their world.
     Looking through eyes pulled into slits and
implementing the street tough walk, the "Don't
bother me" attitude, watching for muggers, drunks,
pimps and cops, I kept a steady pace. Following the
broken concrete walk smelling of yesterday's wine
and winos, I made my way further up the street,
crossing quickly at road crossings and approaching
the skid row house of rooms. The building in which
I made my home particular simply by hanging my
toothbrush within.
     Entering the doorway, I stumbled across winos
still sleeping off the toxins or dying from the drink
itself. I reached down, picking up a good stub of

146

cigarette one had left just far enough out of his
reach that I could claim it. I retreated again. This
time into my room, my realm, my piece of sanity.

The room was a home. Two decades have passed
by and still in all current meanings of the word--it
was home to me. The stained walls and waxless
floors with their checkerboard, once black and
white, now grey and darker grey. The broken
window allowed a major arm of the oak tree next to
the building to grow through it for at least twenty
years, or more. Where, during certain fall seasons,
squirrels would run up and down hiding food for
later devourings.

In one corner, on the northwest side was a
shower curtain hung in a circle, the ring of bar
above substituting for a walled enclosure for the
showerhead and floor drain hidden behind the
curtain. Next to this water closet was the toilet. The
porcelain object left out in the open, with no
attempt made to hide it in shame. Around to the
right on the northeast, was a propane Coleman
stove, on top of a gas range. The range was left
disconnected as were the lights, because I could not
pay the deposit.

Thumbing through the book for a dry match, I lit
a candle on the stove and the tobacco stub and
looked to the southeast. I saw the branch and missed
the squirrels I'd seen only a few months earlier. I
walked across to the southwest, back near the door I
had entered through, finished smoking the butt and
stubbed it out on the floor. Taking the roll of cover
from under my arm, I gently spread it over the
sprung coil mattress and wrapped in it like a cocoon
once again, closing my eyes, remembering the
dryer and the smell of Downy softener the man had
used to take the stiff residue from his work clothes.
The man with his big work jacket and red cap pulled
down near his ear tops. The one with a stiff leg and
dark brown skin the color of his gloves.

I'd seen him before and others like him. Those men with clothes too dirty for their wives', or mothers', washing machines. Those with women strong enough to tell them that they should wash them themselves. Handing them quarters and dimes for the washers and dryers. Those that found quiet, as I did, from the loneliness and unattractive environment of the coin-ops. Those that came home tired, dirty and who just wanted to rest. Those whose women knew this and gave them that right, that trusting, expecting they really would go to the laundromat and not to the massage parlour two blocks up on the right.

I pulled up the cover over my face and head like a hood and made my cheeks feel the heat fading away rapidly. The fade occurring much more quickly than I would have preferred it to. Keeping the wrap around me I crawled over to blow the candle out and snuggled down to sleep. I promised to remember the song my mind composed as I entered the dreamtime. Upon morning's break I would. As I always did. During the sleep I dreamed of many things. I imagined myself a great invisibility. A void of ghost like creation. One who could be in two worlds at once. I dreamed of those I left in my other home. That home of long ago, before I ran away from that world.

Two shots thudded and four sirens screamed breaking the dreams into fractured fragments. I had to keep one eye closed when checking the street below, through the glassless pane, in order to insure the continuum of dream progress. To keep the shape fluid and constant in the inner realms. The train of night thought. Somewhere in the night, I heard an old man crying. Only by this time I was so locked into the paralysis of sleep I could no longer distinguish interior from exterior sound effects. The banging of the steam pipes above, below and through the room intruded deeply enough to make

148

separation possible once again.

My bones ached beneath the thin skin covering them. My right knee, elbow and neck carrying pain from the cold, frosty air, now filling the room in the first light of day. I hurried over to the radiator trying again to repair the valve. Using a cloth, I gripped hold turning it as hard as I could. Today was the day that the rusted metal would finally give. Rather than releasing heat, the metal on the valve handle gave itself and the handle deteriorated into my thin hand. I banged hard on the pipe hoping the super, downstairs two floors, would hear me and turn up the boiler. I wondered why they would only turn it on once a day, in the early morning, and then not again until another day break. I decided that the other tenants must have their propane turned on. Or perhaps, if their radiators worked, it was enough to heat them all one time. For seven dollars a week I couldn't really complain. They would have had to haul me off to juvenile detention if I'd continued sleeping under bridges, or in used car lots. There was no turning back, not now.

Letting the blanket drop from my shoulders, I slid it from myself and laid it on the pipe. The pipe itself extended up the wall from the floor to the ceiling. I wrapped it tight around this grey metal pipe, which smelled of steam, and tied it into a knot for later use. Then taking the only worn out terry motel towel down from the shower rod, I turned on the tap inside and undressed stepping into hot water from the boiler steam. My joints and skeleton relaxing tension and my eyes closed again in relief from the socket pull.

The water pressure was actually very low, but good enough for the purpose of warming the body. The water itself dense, but not rusty as in the truck stop showers and without the brown, yellow, lingering oxide colors to coat hair and skin. This water, at times, was almost white instead of clear, but left the hair virtually rinsed, not caked in sodas or salts.

There were four shavings of soap left on the little metal soap dish. I took all of these and held them in my fingers under the hot water until they were soft. I then pressed them together and rolled them into a ball of soap to wash with. When finished, I could take my fingers and press indentations into the ball to make it resemble the fancy soap balls I'd seen in a store window once when I'd walked in a town with my dad. I wondered how he was and if he was mad at me for running away from them. Running here. Where I could hide out and hear true blues musicians play on street corners on clear nights without the rains of the night before. Where Mississippi Fred McDowell visited and Wet Willie had a place four blocks away, near the college. Where the music could fill my bones and no one waking up fighting would fight with me because I was alone.

I pretended the water was finger touches of ghosts, or some other friendly being, helping my back relax and my neck respond to the slight pressure. I pulled back the curtain and dried off the best that I could with the towel. I rinsed out the clothes I'd taken off underneath the showerhead and wrung them out. I shook them out and snapped them in the air to flatten out the wrinkles and hung them over the rod above, next to the towel. Crossing to the mattress, I turned around the peach crate I used for a dresser and took out the clothes I'd rinsed the day before and pulled them on.

I lay back onto the bed and pulled out a notepad and ink pen to write the songs I developed in my head. To capture the lines of lyric that made sense to me, knowing no one else would ever hear them unless they found me dead. But that didn't matter. That wasn't the point at all. I lived with the compulsion to write and the life I was handed

150

required an outlet for survival. The thread to the
other world surrounding me. I wondered if Jesse Ed
Davis lived like me, if B.B. King or Miles knew this
place before, or others like it. If anyone really
knew what we were like, those of us who ran away
from hardship to take refuge on the streets, those of
us who searched for heat in the night.

When I felt enough relief, I stopped recording
the lines on paper and rose to record the day. The
songs composed directly from the environment and
events of this place and those memories of before.
In the hall, a young stray dog searched for food. I
petted him, lifted and carried him for a little while
telling the pup to stay around and that I'd bring
him something. I stepped over the drunks lined up
the stairs and went out into the light of day. The dog
was pitiful, I thought, and I wanted to care for him.
My heart palpitated when I considered my assumed
responsibility. He has to eat, I told myself. I saw a
cop cruise around the block and tried to look harder,
older, than I was. I tried to reverse the paranoia
cramping my nerves and muscles. I didn't like
taking advantage of kindness. Sometimes I had to. I
fought the shakiness of my fingers and knees. I
argued the sickness of my gut and pretended it was a
normalcy.

Keeping my eyes and face down, I made my way
to the convenience store on the corner. The man
inside gave me some bread and probably watched me
steal the Alpo dog food hamburgers for the stray. I
slipped the box up my shirt, underneath my jacket,
and said nothing. He gave me some more bread and
I talked with him for a long time promising to sing
with him at night in the back of the store where he
played steel guitar sometimes. He reminded me of
the father of one of the people I had worked with in
the fields of North Carolina. I remembered my
family struggling in poverty and the disastrous
effects of my mother's chronic mental illness on all

151

of us. He was a black man with a kind smile and the greatest laughter that held your attention and on occasion caused your lips to spread into grins.

I promised to return, stuck the bread in my jacket pocket and thanked him with the sincerity one thanks those who lift them from the grave and give them new life and sustenance. I walked backwards out the door, eyes darting corner mirrors, promising myself I would replace the dog food amount somehow. I think it was $1.69 back then, though it seemed like a hundred dollars. I thought I would sweep the floors for him at night when he played.

I walked back to the rooming house and whistled for the dog when I reached the third floor landing. It came out of hiding and I gave it one burger. I told the brown mutt it would most likely get sick if I didn't ration it out to him as I did when I ate a full meal after months of scraps. This was a problem. Having enough food to eat, enough to go around. Where I had come from our meals consisted of commod cheese and macaroni. We had never seen any cut of meat other than hamburger and rarely wild game. I justified my not being able to feed myself on my own without handouts, or stealing, by comparing it to what I had eaten before. I knew the food at my dad's home would go further now and they would actually be much better off. I justified food should be free anyway.

The dog lay at my door throughout the morning and was there when I returned at noon. I fed it another cake of pressed Alpo and stroked its head naming it Tip for the spots on its tail and toes. I brought back a pack of shoe laces and a bandanna this time and made it a woven collar and adopted it as my own. I told the mutt he was free to go as I, myself, was a reckless sort of soul and could pack up anytime.

I had found a dollar on the street, on the second

152

trip out and had gone to a 7-11, down five blocks south, to get the laces and cloth. I did not buy these items first. First, I got a package of salt and when they gave me change I insisted I had given them a ten, not a one, dollar bill and convinced them to give me nine more bills. I bought the ties and hanky, leaving seven dollars remaining for rent. This was a weekly flim-flam I devised, or conjured up, in order to keep the room. It was easy. There were always different clerks, on different shifts, different chain stores--untraceable. A common practice for street kids in techniques of survival, even at what might seem to be an extremely young age to people outside this world. Chain stores being open to lifting. They were part of the national world that those like me did not belong to. They passed by the street, or neighborhood, protection code. I didn't need money any other time and could get paper goods from the coin-op's restrooms in fairly good supply.

I left the pup in the hallway and went downstairs to slide the seven under the door of the super's residence. I included a short note to identify the sender. This way I didn't have to deal with the obese, macho, man who lived in this place with us, but who wasn't quite the same. I had heard he had good furniture with velvet throws over his couch from the guy who delivered mail through the slots on the door. The slots were all carefully numbered, but the mail just fell in a pile on the other side anyway.

I went home to my room and let the door remain cracked so that I could see the pup. I took down the blanket and wrapped it over my shoulders and neck around my jacket. I sat down on the floor to draw with charcoal from the street and to let the music in my mind loose on to the notebook of lines. The sounds of the day and my walking through it. Back and forth from sketch to lyrics. Charcoal to pen.

Both black in color and black inspired, though I was
not and did not try to be. I enjoyed their company,
generosity, and love for sound and beauty in
common things. Being a light-skinned
Huron/Tsalagi Indian/French Canadian/Portuguese
thirteen year old, forced into adulthood early on, I
had plenty of my own richness in culture.

I drew a picture of the Chiricahua Geronimo,
from memory, the best I could do. I knew at the time
I must be thinking of myself because the arms in
the picture were like rails. His were probably not as
small as mine since he was much older than my
crude portrayal.

The lyric went something like this:

> I'm so full of your promises
> promise of being with you
> yes I'm full of your promises
> promises won't come true
> if you've got something more to say
> I'll be waiting on you
> cause I'm so full of your promises
> but I'm still dreamin' they're true
> you know that black is black, and white
> is white
> I know you've got something to
> promise me tonight
> Yeah, I'm so full of your promises
> promises don't come true.

And on so.

The dog wagged its tail and I tossed it the last
piece of food. The sweet, sweet, soft sounds of a
saxophone came drifting up through the iron fire
escape outside the window. They drifted along the
tree limb and into this room. The room filled with a
melody of rhythms so satisfying to my ears. I tilted
my head back and smiled. I did have a home. This
was my place at that time. Attached to sounds like

landscapes. Bound to moods like structures
providing safety. I was alone, but never really
alone. I heard a picker start to play across the hall
in another room. He blended in with the sax as did
the old man crying from the night before, as he
pressed the blues harp to his lips and began to blow.

PERCHERON NAMBE MORNING

A.A.Hedge Coke   for Art Harvey , Travis and Vaughan

dust, leaves twirling
whirlpool
up off road
under wheels
undercarriage
automotive   winds
turning,   lifting
giving force to such
delicate   particles
ends attached in former
position to branch
soft paper thin petal-
like reds and golds
much as the mane swings
blows back from higher
plane winds   percheron   gold
mane that red percheron
on the right
the north side
you've seen her
in the early morning
when it's snowing she
raises her dignity
laughing at motorists
distressed by ice
and Pueblo patrol cars
we catch in peripheral
focus   signal   turn the
halogens off and on
on and off   until
they code the signal
distress signal
approaching tribal police
traffic trap
commuting the
35 mph racket

156

through Nambe
Pojoaque turn   50
Tesuque Bingo/Pull-Tabs
long before the lodge
turned stone   near Camel Rock
before the Congested Area in
approach to the
City of the Oldest Catholic Church in North America
we convey these
danger signs   to
local yokels   perhaps even
tourists   if we're in mood
consideration
strange nation
neither of us belong
though   we do stay
in close   proximity to
these *other* Native peoples
very different than where we
come from   still the same
only   *sometimes*   though
they know the patrol
man he's their cousin
all of theirs'
they know this whirl
these leaves   rising now
before our heated grill
Chevy 4X   '92
they know the percheron
she steals the scenery easily
with her laughter and turns
pitching hoof and tail
in mockery   indispensable humor
she takes this morning
under grey the shade of nickel
to cloud the stress enabling
me to speak to you of
beauty

DOG ROAD WOMAN

A. A. Hedge Coke   *f or Derya*

They called you
grandma
Maggie   like
Maggie Valley
I called   on you
for your knowledge
of pieced cotton
I worked clay
to pottery
and thread   to weave
but   had no frame
nor understanding
of pattern
in quilting.
Climbing high
in sacred wood,
which feeds   the
di ni la wi gi   u no do ti,
I captured hickory
twigs   you wanted
for a toothbrush
to dip snuff.
Ninety-two year old
leathered fingers
caressed stitch
and broadcloth .
into blanket.
You with your apron
and bonnet
and laughter
at *gold dollars*
and processed meats.
You who taught
me to butcher
without waste

and who spun
stories   on your
card   whenever   I
would   listen,
we fashioned stars

CASTING VESSEL

A. A. Hedge Coke   for Cheryl, Scott, Sarah, & Sam

Pamlico
Sound
flamingos,
hot pink
gentle grace   braced
on one leg
against
feathered snow,
swans wearing
black masks.
Spanish moss hanging,
netting tall
trees surrounded
by kudzu,
greenest vines creeping,
as we net
jumping mullet
and shrimp,
drift nets and
casting nets
across the bank
on the Atlantic,
the outer banks
of Carolinas,
highest corner
of Bermuda's
Triangle,
up past Emerald Isle.
The voices
of a thousand
waterfowl
carry our boat
with waving motion
back to you.
We gig flounder
and scoop up

live scallop,
with their
iridescent rim
of blue eyes shining
from the very
edge of protection.
Not a crease
on the water,
the breeze remains
among the tree tops
kissing fluffs
of swan clouds
slipping from
the blue, blue
sound of sky
above   dotted
by   wing,
goose and
diving ducks,
those who
pierce the
crest of waves
to fish with
skill of pelicans   by
the sound of
sky and sea
surrounding and
holding all this
sacred blue bowl
of intricate design.

HASANI

A. A. Hedge Coke   to Susan Power

Hasani
half-side
waste/osta
if it's good
if it lasts
isnala mani
waste/osta
if it's lost
if it's bad
isnala mani win
a choice, a decision
to make things
so much easier
on the mind
and heart
to lessen the
heaviness
the burden.
Freedom
like a zintcala
cante o hupahu
until then
isnala
until then
peace of mind
freedom of nagi
and easiness
of cante
until then
lonesomeness
but   the loneliness
will be
sheltered
not exposed,
not vulnerable.

Protected, safe
personal
until then
life will
be perceived
from the
individual
mind
seeking

THE SOUND OF JADE STRIKING

A. A. Hedge Coke

eluding passion
dancing   back
with two-step time
further away from
chance   of desire
and torch of pain
slight neglect
of your gasping
and smothering touch
shouldered resistance
brought on by
stairs spiraling
and unexpected realization
exposing your
mirrored intention
just seconds before
the refrain begins

FINE POINT

A. A. Hedge Coke

Often pain accompanies relapse
in sequence replay
those fractional memory responses
relative to spans, or seconds, timed
retrieving spent focus on
design aligning your face
within the place between
shoulders, lower, behind ribs
that very definitive beat
once thriving, now hollow,
indefinite in rhythmic
pattern, palpitations four quarter
bent and separated to half time.
Regular, common, occurrence
in the mourning light which
creeps through the jagged split shade
shadowing the pane shielding
fresh air encompassing new.
Coincidental resplendencey in strobe
flashbacking illustrations on lobe
to frontal conceptions
those mistranslations I link you to.

ICE

A.A.Hedge Coke

stripping   sleeting scales
sheets that slide   so suddenly
apart   without fraying
layers   compiled by multitudes
emotions   deluding strength
in skin   I am a skin
beneath skin and   by skin
frozen into thick   panes
the pain almost   too much
overwhelming   on the final
the most   utmost   solitary stand
its brink approaching rapidly
water forcing paths through night
hardened ripples   petrified in time
those droplets protruding   fast flow
down   lacrimal duct   the inlet
into   this   iced edge facial cheek
river bank   in bone   breaking
fracture   in   structure   bold
like the strongest ship plows
the sea   as the tractor plow
breaks waves   turning the soil
affording imminent changes
metamorphic   existence   it goes
almost unnoticed   though the
last time it occurred   wounds
still linger   un-evaporated
unchallenged   uncovered   unhealed
this freely quaking tremor
eroding   stone   catastrophic results
lying still   so very still   chunks plunge
beneath lower limbs   the sycamore
she swings her sleeves   slowly below
caress by winds   witness the
wiping of tears   let not the
masquerade conceal notions   flowing

166

vast oceans   for appearance   sake
screaming   pure tonal height
harmonies   bells taken by far
nearer   to destiny   to denial
she whispers   the echo   light
the sound hangs delicately   upon
fairest breeze   wisps begin
spinning   reeling   turning afar
so far   to here   let the
beauty   begin   scaling madness
rope   in loops   sailing winding
grasping circles   air   bringing in
rounding up   the lost   the
abandoned   the abused   the forgotten
let not be forgotten   the
least of all the pitiful
bring
the simple spark
life lighting   flickering flare
shining so simply   most extraordinarily
its simplicity   ticking   the clock
faces itself   in time that   trickle
edges through   these plates   panes
glass ice   face the sheer dew   held
in gasps   in wakening   in display
she sighs with   e f f o r t   with
heavy   heart   heaving   air   pumping
lung   heart   thump   thumping
through this embodiment   this
wonderful enclosure   between
skin   under   water   the fresh water
is blood   though salty in tear
river to ocean   ocean   emotion-al
release   tension   pain   madness
the effect   of the moon   on tides
within the body of earth   of man
let the tiny   minuscule drop   be the
spark   life connecting
breaking barriers   frozen in this

world time   beyond the illusion
we dwell in   ring the tingles
the bell's echoes   on glass tolls
the ice rings as does the edge
glass   champagne glass
by touch   delicate and round
ringing   as ripples   on the stream
beneath this famous facade
the tear   reaches   deep into   the
frozen edge   just as the water breaks
the thick blue bulges   ice
congregating   on this river   they
break apart   with sound
with pristine perfection   with   enormous
slide   and with deepest grief
listen to the sound   heal
to the breaking   erase pain
touch the very moment
emergence   to this next
point   in awareness   in bringing
this juxtaposition   paradox   paradigm
lips touch softly   blow fluffs
white dandelions   across   ice
spring to winter   in
the quiet   the strength   the river
facing   ever facing   self   immediate
a sense   shattering bergs   mountains
ice   relief   a spirit swallows

RADIO WAVE MAMA

A. A. Hedge Coke   *for Art Harvey and those close*

transistor radios
planted firmly
against ears
the children
smothered under
pillows over
their heads   and
shoulders
escaping the sounds of "ssssss"
and vulgarities screamed
they didn't know the
true meaning of
and invented   replacement
definitions   from
expansive imaginations
when the vocal tensions   invaded
the safer   place
of refuge
under covers
over lumps   in
shared bed they composed
songs to   avoid
rhythms of madness

and poems to
describe hysteria   or
to rearrange
perspectives   of   life
their life
their metaphoric
existence
cropped by
delusions
when the wrath
dispensed overflow
they crawled on
the floor
before school and
scrubbed the baseboards
with toothbrushes
and Babo
in accordance with
their mother's
instruction from   thorax
or from the   radio
waves   that controlled
her mind,   her thought
processes and processed her individual dialect
and dialectic statements

intended specifically
to instill private belief
of the megalomania
knowledge factors
she alone had
privy to   in her
babies   those children
she bore   and   who
were expected to
bear witness   to
her testimonies
her, "Electronic computer
PUP-PE-TRY!
Comb your
hair   children!"   informing
those surrounding her
and surrounded by   her
voice
apart from the crowd
apart of   their lives
they walked two
aisles over from her
in the Piggly Wiggly
listening to her
through the aisles and
hearing the comments

from strangers
from   pass-her-bys
in shock,   in awe,
in obliviation   to
her informative
speeches and semi-
silenced whispersssss
breaking silence
absolute with "ssssss"
and vulgarities
"Get off my vulva.
You Damn, dirty,
pimps. United States
government   prop-a-gan-da."
she says and
grabs a box of
Kellogg's Corn Flakes   for
her husband
"Quit raping me
with radio waves."
She orders and
pushes the cart
with the broken
wheel skidding
slowly up the
row of   canned

goods and she
screams, "Buggers,
PIMPS, IBM,
Esso, United States
Air Force,   You are
ALL in this together!"
and they say
"listen to that woman,
who is she???"
as if they didn't
know and she
whispers, "Sssssso,
you think you have
fooled me with thisssss
plot, thissss sssssscheme
to rule my mind.
Not thissss Time!" Then
she wheels into the check out and
exchanges pleasantries
with the checker
whom she calls
"Dear" and gets upset
if she isn't addressed
by her last name
with formal prefix

the children try the
coin return on all
vending   machines
within preschool and
early elementary
grade reach of extremities
they run to the
Studebaker as she
carries out   the
brown paper sacks
with nineteen cent loaves of
bread and food for
five for a few
days   which in their
reality is supposed
to last them at least
a week, or two
and could very possibly as their
mother rants too •
much to boil eggs
and they make the
cheese and macaroni
independently by
three and try when
they are younger toddlers

and due to the
anorexic condition
of little sister   who
has the syndrome
at least a decade
before   the   word   is
coined for marketplace
they crawl over each
other   to the back
the very rear of
the wagon,   the middle
seat occupied by one
the oldest child
the other two in
the rear and the
other three,   or four,
dead at birth or
shortly thereafter as
the children have already
been informed by
their mother while
tucking them in at
night   when she thinks
it opportune to
implant this knowledge
she alone walks with

she keys the ignition
rolling the engine past
sputters and knocks
the children appreciate
the pink, so pink, fin-tailed
Buick   next to them
and wish they had
a newer model like
that   it looks like
a space ship to them
seven years before
the moon landing
where their mother
sometimes   resides now
applying foot to pedal
she squeals out   in
reverse   carts scattering
her path   and begins,
"Never, never, never,
before   here   were we
violated by these
computer puppets
these objects of technology!"
and the children fish
through sacks   for
animal crackers   they

176

threw into the cart
when she wasn't looking
knowing she wouldn't
know the difference
because she was "busy"
they pass by the
light   before   the train
crossing,   "Do you
see anything?" the
light flashing and boards, striped,
falling   in front of the
grill, "No, of course not."
older sister says
and she proceeds
the train pouring on speed
as if there were no
time to s-l-o-w for
passenger cars
blowing its whistle
of Santa Fe and Atchinson
Topeka and Ashland City
Tennessee   and they pass
the rear end tail pushed by
winds off of the rail in
time, in time, with the
beat of the rail

da-nan-da-nan-da-nan-da-nan
the heartbeat of railroad
suddenly the wooden
bar goes through the back
　CHKCHKCHKCHKCHK
　PINGGGGGGPINGGGGGG
windshield on the far
side　　and the children gasp
for breath and eat more
cookies　　looking carefully
for witnesses　　they tell
her, "go on, no one saw"
and she complies　　it
has begun to sleet
and the ice rain is
falling on the streets
on cars　and on the
car of children　and
their mother　　or
imposter　of mother
they're not really
sure yet　and it
freezes　patches of
the front　　windshield
and sleets　through the
back　　little sister

imagines the ice accumulations
windows   to another   place
she traces in her   mind
and sings "jimmy crack corn"
and "mama may have" to
herself   her brother hits
and pulls her hair and
sister sticks out her
tongue   she smiles
and sings louder   her
mother turning the
lyrics around, "Jimmy
Crack Corn the Master,
the Master, the Master,
the president of the
United States and the president
of the AMA"   and they
go down iced streets
the tobacco road
they follow   the girl
turns to Native American lullabies
her dad sings her to
sleep with   and the
mother says, "Don't you
make fun of your father!
He has a beautiful voice!"

and she is only trying
to sound   like him
to get away   from her
and the mother says,
"Buckle your seatbelts
the buggers are going
to make me wreck."
and the older sister
takes off her seatbelt
and dives headfirst into the floorboard
ensuring complete concussion
she is unconscious now
the baby boy is
strapped into a belt
by   little sister and
she glances out
to see a blue blurrr
of a car   through   the
iced windshield   and her
mother's concentration
on hitting this car
head on   and   she grasps
the back of the middle
seat and hangs on for
life, her life,   though
she doesn't really want

it saved   and by seven years of age
will be slitting her
wrists   and surviving that
anyway   because she
has the survival skills
the urgency to maintain
through anything   the
adaptability   of children
of the chronically
insane   parental influence
she grabs and holds   hard
and her mother slowly,
carefully, deliberately,
drives into the innocent
car   steering   slammmming
into the car which
tears off the front fender,
driver's door, rear wheel and
breaks the glass
next to little sister's
cheeks   and careening off
the shoulder   trying
to steer away from
this mad woman
they assume   has lost
control of the wheel

when quite the opposite
is true   the control
is within her, or the
voices she hears,   or the
place of their   origin
her mind
the mother is now
unconscious, liquid red eyes,
canyon gashed brow flowing in concussion
the older sister   is still   asleep
the baby is eating a
cookie   the other car's
passengers walking over
little sister pretends
to be knocked out
the police come
it is snowing and a dark complected
man looks through
the broken rear windows
and sees the rail road
crossing bar
the little sister   waves to him
and he calls her
from the car
she sits in his police car
and calls her dad

on the two way
"one adam twelve,
is this daddy?
one adam twelve,
calling daddy.
daddy are you in?"
the father asks
"Whose phone are you
on, who   dialed   for   you?"   "the copper's,
it's his"   and they   exchange
information of
insanity   of
split realities of
the mother   and
the children   the dad and the cop
little sister smiles
at all the people
gathering   and is proud
she could use a
police phone   and remember
the number   no one
ever taught her
she learned to memorize   by
teaching herself numbers and letters
she is three

she will always
remember this day
days   of   perspectives
that   other
people   will
never   be able   to
relate   to without
an Artaud   in the
family   themselves
and when she grows
she will feed the
homeless   schizophrenics
she sees   wandering
streets   and   tobacco roads
and know that without her
father   her   mother
would have ended up
down the same path
of the pitiful   who
walk the other side
while they reside here
those that see   the   s p a c e
between second and third
dimensional arts   and speak it
the children witness
and play transistor radios

DIGS XII -- excerpt from novel

A. A. Hedge Coke   *for my dad*

Brad held onto the crew as long as possible in attempt to utilize the air time as well as possible. Even to the point of following Phil and Rena to the van when the equipment was being put away. "You'll have to clear the area," Phil said, "we need to get this equipment to the station now. It's raining." As the van doors closed behind them the mob began rocking the van once again. Randy said, "Let them go. It won't help us to become violent at this point. They have control of the media, for now." The crowd let a small space around the van deepen to allow the van to pull out from their midst. Brad snickered at them as they pulled away.

Rena tore off the wig as soon as they escaped visibility of the crowd. Her long hair swayed as she shook it loose from the concentrated ball she had it clipped in. Phil told her, "You did a great job." "You were pretty convincing yourself," she said, "could've fooled me."

The rains poured as they hadn't for some years. California had begun periods of severe droughts back in the last century. There would be breaks in the dryness, however, nothing like the old monsoon seasons that occurred prior to 1985. These rains filled the streets and gutters, seemingly washing away the filth of the city. Even the rains were so filled with poisons they were unhealthy, at best. Acid rains had completely ruined certain areas that had been filled with small animals at one time. These creatures no longer existed and as a result neither did animals that depended on them in the chain of what had, at one time, been nature.

Scheduled to meet with Swimmer later that evening, they decided to finish up the day at the station and check into the results of the other shoot. Phil took care to remove the tape from the camera and place it is his personal belongings, rather than that of the station's. Rena took notes as to what had transpired at the cemetery. The van splashing water up from its fenders onto the curb as they drove back to work.

Brad told the crowd he would meet with them back at the pub after he went home to check on his uncle. He climbed into the car with Randy who seemed to be a bit miffed at the way things had gone saying, "I think this is getting out of hand. I hope you know what you're getting us into." His cousin put his arm around his shoulder as he drove and said, "Don't worry. It's for your dad, and for Grandma. We have to do this. You'll see. Wait until you see the news, then you'll see some changes happening. This could be war!"

Swimmer drove the pick-up toward the Stephanie's neighborhood. He felt she'd be more comfortable in her own home. A laser flashed advertisements across the clouds. Normally this form of sales was reserved for nights, but in the case of dark skies some Mainstreamer companies took advantage of the opportunity to show their trademarks. Their symbols demonstrating a purely commercialized reality emblazoned soft drink emblems across the overcast spanse of sky.

"Are you taking me home?" She asked Swimmer. "Unless you'd rather go somewhere else to talk." "No, that's alright." She suddenly felt like a small child and very small physically sitting between the two of them. She felt no resistance, but rather a surrender in situation. The fear and apprehension were slowly trickling away from her and replacing it was a calmness and curiosity.

They pulled up to her complex and the men followed her upstairs to her unit. She offered them fresh coffee and juice. Realizing they hadn't eaten and that it was passed the noon hour she went to the kitchen and returned with ultra-waved hot sandwiches. Microwaves had been replaced by ultra-

186

waves when too many people had problems with electronic devices helping their organs to operate. Brought on by the revamping of handicapped accessibility laws and statutes. This was around the turn of the century, about the time aerosol sprays had finally been banned and permanently removed from the consumer market. Mostly due to the environmental hazards such as holes in the ozone and defoliage of tropical zones from the heat waves following the tears in the atmosphere layers.

Swimmer and Ball thanked her for offering them coffee and food and welcomed the chance to relax a minute and eat before talking. Swimmer wondered how Ball's testimony about factual past occurrences involving her own father would affect her. He worried about her vulnerability. He hoped that the last twenty-four hours hadn't been too hard on her and that she was tough enough to go the mile. She appeared, at least to him, to be breaking. He looked around her home and took particular notice in her paintings and sculpture. He wondered when she so obviously had artistic talents, why then, would she pursue such anti-creative work. Thinking he may be mistaken he asked bluntly, "Who is the artist?" pointing his finger around the apartment at many pieces of work. "I was." She answered. "Was, why do you refer to it in past tense." "It has been in the past for a number of years that's why. No time for frivolous enjoyments. I only have time for my work now." "Some people consider this work." Swimmer added and let the conversation go as he finished his second sandwich.

Ball thanked her again for feeding them as did Swimmer and she cleared the remaining plates out of their way. Ball invited her to sit by him as he spoke. She took her coffee with her and sat in the overstuffed chair next to the one he, himself sat in. Swimmer maintained his seat across from them, being unwilling to intrude on such a private

187

moment.

He felt great empathy for what she must be going through and seeing how pitiful she actually was, forgave her for her part in the hinderance of their cause and their struggle for survival as a people. He prayed in his mind for Ball to have the right words to say to her for her to understand and know the truth. He hoped she hadn't been too brainwashed in the assimilation program for full reversal. Only time would tell.

Ball began by telling her he thought the world of her and she had always been near him in his heart, even though the years had been long between them. He explained there was a reason for his absence from her life and he asked if there was a possibility to change all of that adding, "You can with hold your answer until I have told you everything."

"Your father lives on in my heart as I am sure he does in your own. We were very close, like brothers. In fact, we had adopted one another when we were young men. I honestly thought he would be with me here as long as I walked this earth. When he was killed a part of me went with him. My fiance was killed by the same people. I loved her so much. I can't really explain to you my feelings. It's something I hope I never see you walk through. I hope that when you find love, it can last a lifetime for you. To lose someone that close to your heart can ruin you or change you beyond going back to who you were, or thought you were, before. It is a sobering experience."

Stephanie was taken by emotion as he spoke. She immediately excused herself to the kitchen to get some more coffee. As soon as she got into the other room she cried, silently, holding back as much as possible. She had a very clear image of her father and Ball. They were standing next to one another and her father had his arm wrapped around Ball's shoulder in friendship. This is how she remembered him. Other images of him flashed before her eyes; her mother and father walking hand in hand, her father helping her learn to build a fire and look for birds in the brush in the early morning, her father laughing and smiling a smile as big and as free as the smile she witnessed on Swimmer's face. She missed him. She couldn't make herself believe he had actually been murdered. How could it be? Why wouldn't she have known by now. Why wouldn't her mother have told her.

After drying her eyes and controlling her emotions, she brought the coffee cups back, filled to the brim, and took her place next to Ball. Swimmer kept his eyes down out of respect to what his friend was going through to speak of this again, after so many years. He was used to him going through the hardest of times with him, but this time was different somehow. It wasn't just the two of them and it involved someone who had no understanding of these things to prepare herself with.

Ball went on, '"We were making a safeguard bunker around the area we were held up in. Two men, members of the Coalition of Commerce, C-men, Mainstreamers, came around from behind us while we had shovels raised. There was no time whatsoever when they gunned him down, from behind. I watched him fall from the corner of my eye, I threw down my shovel and tried to go to him. I was in shock, thought there was something I could do for him. That's when I got hit, here," He said pointing to his left side, "I guess they wanted my heart, but my ribs caught the bullet. Whenever I feel it give me some pain, I remember clearly and I know I'll never sell-out like some of them did. I will always remember that day."

He stopped for a while, just sat there thinking.

You could almost see the day he spoke of playing in his eyes, like a movie. The lines on his face showed the years that had passed since then like battle wounds. Stephanie wanted to hug him, but didnt know him well enough anymore and didn't know if he would appreciate it or if it would make him feel weak. She did not want to insult him in any way. After a while he began again.

"My fiance was in the shack behind us, helping you mother board up the windows. She was a feisty one, never backed down from any Mainstreamer, would say anything to anyone if it would help The People. She had principal and that stood before anything, even her own happiness. She was reclusive by nature, but the cause she believed in would not allow her to be invisible. It often threw her into the forefront of conflict and she was more verbal then most of us then so she often became the spokesperson by request of the same people she stood for. And she was most beautiful, to me. I loved her." He paused a moment before going on, as if remembering her beauty above all the pain.

"She was boarding up a window when they knocked in a back door. They killed her slowly, not allowing her the dignity of a quick death. When your mother tried to stop them they knocked her out. They mutilated her body when they were through and took your mother with them, she was still out cold. I hate to tell you this, but they raped her."

At this Stephanie leaped forward, "What?" she screamed. Her face crumpled, her brow twisted forming faint lines, her lips parted slowly, her voice demanded, "Who were they? I want to know! Who did this?" "Mainstreamers working for the Coalition of Commerce." "You know who they are, please tell me."

190

"I can't, not right now. You could get yourself into some serious problems if you knew. That's why your mother never told you, she vowed she wouldn't. The last thing she would want is to lose another relative for the likes of them. I know who they are and they will pay, when it is time. That will not finish the issue though, as long as there are Mainstreamers there will be those like them. Those that stand before justice and call themselves justice. Those who fool the people and themselves. It won't end until they are gone from here, for good."

Stephanie began to weep openly. She held back from making any sounds but, her tears flowed like streams across her face and both men had trouble looking at her. They both lowered their heads, then Ball began crying, too. Swimmer reached out toward Stephanie and asked her if he could do anything to help her. She stared at him and said, "I want to know the truth. Can you tell me the truth." He knew they had her at this point, but regretted the method they'd been forced to use to make her remember. He only wished there'd been some other way. He found peace of mind in knowing now that she remembered she would have a chance to lead a real life, to leave the dead world and join them in the living.

A. A. Hedge Coke   *for Janelle and Sandy*

Phil and Rena headed down 101 Freeway North, toward Northridge campus. The sky blackened, imitating a starless night. Phil placed a compact disc into the player, turning the volume to six and a half, allowing the sounds to ease the pain of freeway driving. Laser advertisements strobed across the rolling clouds above. He remembered seeing Minute Men missiles being tested here, years before, and how they colored the skies much as the lasers did now. The advertisements were operated off discs, too. Everything seemed disc-oriented; computer discs, compact discs, meal programmer discs, laser discs, the list was endless. He thought, *"The world is flat--its on disc."*

A yellow 2020 Miraculous Mercedes coup passed by them in the *number two* lane. Two older Mainstreamer women occupied the vehicle. They were close enough for Rena to see that the interior was pure leather. She noticed the women were extremely calm in the heavy traffic. Heads rested back on contoured head rests. She assumed they had air-pump lumbar support seating filled with the precise amount of air to fit their bodies like a rubber mold. *The wealthy can afford to be calm,* she thought. Something she had realized when reviewing classic twentieth century poetry by Leslie Scalapino. *The oppressed and impoverished must make noise to survive,* she added to the interior dialogue in her mind. She longed for the day when N.P.I.I.C. would be able to dismantle the Coalition for Commerce altogether. For, *the day this imperialistic reign comes to a final end.*

They had borrowed the station van again to take this short trip to the Anthro Labs in order to locate their contact *on the inside*. Dubbed the code name "Little Bird," the contact was anonymous, even to them. The only ones who knew this person's identity were Swimmer and Ball. Neither was available and they needed to check on Thompson--before the meeting this evening.

Travelling the lost world of Los Angeles, Phil remembered hearing stories of the Natives that used this same road as a path before any Intruders saw this place. 99% of the freeway system was made directly over roads, made over paths the Natives had used. He thought of the first Invaders who called war upon The People *under the name of their Catholic God.* The priests that enslaved so many hundreds of men, women and children. The two flaming arrows shot into the mission's thatched roof up the coast when The People who had been captured were being treated cruelly and dying. The girls and women separated from their husbands, boyfriends, uncles, grandfathers. The People, here, who had no word for war in their vocabulary, nor known enemies of other tribes. The People who had a peaceful existence and lifestyle since their emergence into this world. These females being abused by priests and their men, having babies of mixed blood that carried these priests' names. The technique of the arrows had been show to them by a Nation from their east, in the great plains, Lakota or Cheyenne who came here in search of shell and trade. They shot the arrows into the roof and The People inside, having to take part in a holiday mass, were set free. But, not for long.

He remembered that the average life-span of a Mission Native was only seven years, no matter how young they were when they were brought in. How all their culture was stripped from them, including language and song. He thought of how the missionaries then had the slave Natives make adobe by mixing straw, mud, sand and water with their feet. Then building more missions with these bricks and, after the two arrow uprising--the only uprising of the entire mission regime--covering the roofs with tile they imported from Mexico. And the Mexicans came and fought Spain and released the Natives from the missions and hired them to work on their rancheros. To duplicate the slave labor, but to be paid for it.

As Phil drove by the concrete world he dwelled in, he also remembered that the Americans, those Euro-Americans who had killed off so many of The People since their arrival came, too. And it became so racist that The People left would claim to be Mexican to avoid the most severe bigotry.

These were thoughts of the forgotten California. The forty-niners, who came and killed Natives for the gold rocks beneath their feet. The Californians who in the roaring twenties put Ishi in a living museum with his murdered wife's belongings next to him to remind him of what had been, and what was gone. Of Native people who had worn capes of brilliantly colored feathers, red, yellow. Who sang songs of blue jays teasing each other and played the rhythm on sticks slit at the end and sounding like buckskin brushing leaves while walking in the forest. People who called to dolphins, to porpoises, who would answer their calling and dance on the waves before them and swim with them whenever beckoned. People who were happy and led a life of leisure. He remembered their peaceful existence and looked around himself in dismay.

"Whats wrong?" Rena asked him. "The world, look at it. The world is wrong. It has been wronged."

194

High above them on a freeway sign the message flashed, *Attention: Gas Masks Required Next Ten Miles.* They reached into the mask box, under the conventional glove box compartment, and pulled the plastic and rubber equipment from within it. Both placed their own masks on, silently without acknowledging the affect it had on them, or the dangers of breathing noxious air.

Rena watched Phil a little more closely. She worried he might become depressed. Almost all Native people had come from families affected somehow by co-dependency, dysfunction, alcohol abuse, or other problems associated with poverty and oppression. Though the last ten, twenty, years had made substantial differences in their paths, the road was a long one to full recovery. It took five hundred and twenty eight years to bring them here, it would take more than twenty to correct the damage of the Euro-World Nations on this continent.

Phil rolled the vinyl covered steering wheel in his palms hand over hand as he exited the freeway onto Reseda Boulevard. The traffic continued to be heavy next to them on either side and they continued toward the campus. There was a flower shop on the right-hand side of Reseda that was selling red and yellow roses laced with palest white baby's breath and fern sprigs. Rena could see them, though because of the pollution, Phil could not. The air was so dense that, at times, you felt as though you were coming out of a cloud bank into a clearing experiencing the difference in visibility between three and five feet. Cars and pedestrians darting in and out of the smog like touches of colors appearing and disappearing from the side lanes and sidewalks. The odor consisted of gaseous fumes, burned rubber and sewage. The

sounds of horns honking was reduced by horn mufflers
on older cars and soft horns on the newer, more
improved, models as a result of the strictly enforced
noise pollution laws. The clouds opened up, once
again, like blankets releasing rain to cleanse this
world. Phil and Rena took off their masks, knowing
that if it rained more than an hour they would not
need them for at least a day after. It seemed unreal
there could be this much pollution in all the advances
and recent adjustments made in the new world,
however, it existed and it wasn't going away
voluntarily.

Nearing Prairie Street, Phil saw the shopping
center that survived the riots of 2010 and remained
open and in the much the same state as it had
originally stood. Several cafes of different origins
lined the walks; Italian, Armenian, Thai, and he
noticed a newer shop he had never seen . "Rena, have
you ever noticed before? Navajo Frybread Feast." He
said pointing to the cafe on her right. "I think they
just put the sign up. I've eaten there before, it's
choice. This is the first time I've seen the sign. I
guess they were waiting to see if the Yuppies across
the road would cause any problems before
advertising." Rena answered him and she
remembered the mouth watering frybread she'd eaten
there with sprinkles of powdered sugar. It was much
different than in her own tribe. The large pancake-
like Navajo style reminded her of tortillas, whereas her
own people's style was smaller pieces rolled and cut
into rectangles or rounded in palms into even smaller
balls of very light bread. The breads having both
sugar and salt in them had a sweet and tart taste
depending on the personal mix. She preferred these
homemade breads to the store-bought mixes of ready

made fry bread of the modern market. Some of the older people, back home, laughed still at the idea of this food going on the open Euro-American market place.

Driving in to the parking lot on the campus filled with cars and trucks and what appeared to be raging Yuppies, Phil was glad they had brought the station's van. *They won't trash this one, they need the media right now.* A voice called out, "Hey, it's that camera man and Red Horse." Another responded, "That's not Red Horse, her hair's too long." As they stepped out of the van and made their way through the crowd Phil complimented the Yuppies on their good behavior during the interview, "Should look good on tape." He said and they crossed over the walks into the lab building. A guard stood ready with a riot suit on and questioned their arrival, "Do you have business here?" Rena showed him a press pass and got them through the doors without any additional problems. The boarded the elevators to go upstairs.

"What do you suppose they are trying to accomplish?" Phil asked. Rena answered, "Probably celebrating their glory at the cemetery. I don't think they've heard the bad news, yet." Going all the way up to the fourth floor they got off the elevator and began looking for Hold-Outs they'd seen around. This was the only way they could think of to determine who the contact was. Rena was uncomfortable passing by gurneys with corpses on them. Corpses tagged at the toe with paper identifying where they were dug up and who they were when they were living and other pertinent information to research. She cringed at the wall filled with skulls being compared for brain capacity, orifices, spaces in the bare bone. "Looks like a trophy room." She said to Phil and he agreed silently.

She remembered the stories during reorganization about the twentieth century President George Bush's father accused of being the culprit who stole Geronimos head and placed it in Yale University as a trophy for the Skull and Bones Fraternity Club. Of what it was like to survive in an era where the Euro-Americans most powerful leaders had no knowledge, or conceptions, of Native People whatsoever. She remembered stories from twenty years before where The People had retaliated and abducted those leaders and fed them commod pork and cheese for a month then released them into their society to demonstrate even a tiny portion in perspective of reservation life.

A voice quietly approached them from behind, "Take the next door to the left." It was a native voice and they followed the subtle orders given them. They pushed open the huge wooden door on the left of the hall and came into a room filled with boxes and shelving. There were counters with test tubes and burners, electric supplies, tape, and other items catalogued carefully as were the boxes.

They turned around at the exact same time and faced a young man. The man had long, black hair braided tightly into two braids and wrapped in red cloth. They had seen him before, many times though neither knew his name or his identity. "Phil, Rena," he said extending his hand. "It's good to meet you. They shook his hand, one at a time, and Phil asked, "And you are?" "Little Bird. I've been watching Thompson all day. He knows too much. I heard him on the phone. I was patched in to his line from another receiver. He knows Swimmer left Red Horse a note. Stark told him, blackmail attempt, I think. He also knows she's with Swimmer and Ball, right now. I think he's got a thing for her. He's getting jealous and worried about the project falling into Hold-Out control." Rena eyed hischiseled face, *young and intelligent,* she thought.

Phil offered, "What is he up to now?" "He's below us on the second floor. He's looking through some of Red Horse's files, but I think most of them are in her home. See." He showed them to a terminal that viewed the Red Horse's lab. "This is what he uses to spy on her. When he doesn't hang around in her doorway." Rena and Phil watched him with Little Bird. They witnessed him pouring through all her cabinets and drawers searching for clues. He was not a happy man.

Rena asked, "Any ideas?" Little Bird smiled and told them to wait there for him. He left them alone in the lab and they continued to watch Thompson on the screen in front of them. In a few moments he returned, "Here's Thompson's personal notes on the digs and on Red Horse. Get them to Swimmer at the meeting tonight. He will be there." They thanked him and put the file inside the rain coat Rena was wearing. "We'll bring them back to you when we copy them." Phil said. "That won't be necessary, these are copies. Thompson wont miss anything that way." Little Bird responded and added, "See you around I've got some work to do before the fire me here. By the way, the main Yuppie is a Stark--Brad." They followed him out into the hall and he showed them the way to the stairwell so that they might avoid Thompson and other Northridgers.

They made it through the building and by the lower-level guard without hesitations. Once they had reached the lot, they still had the Yuppies to contend with. Voices yelled, "Hey! Tape us now! How about an interview, now?" Rena smiled a very disarming smile and kept her hand inside her coat to hold up the file. The yuppies assumed this meant she had a pistol, or stun-phaser, and pulled back away somewhat to let them cross. They climbed into the van and Phil commented on how the oldest tricks still work on the Yuppies and other Mainstreamers. "You saved us," he teased.

The clock above the stereo told them it was time to move on to the meeting. As dark as it was already natural time was hard to tell without the aid of timepiece. Rena said that she wanted to drive and Phil turned over the wheel to her. She threaded drenched Yuppies in the lot and shot out of the campus accelerating speed as she left the area. "Phil, could you make sure we have everything?" She handed him the file and he placed it on the console next to the video tape. "I don't think there's anything else we'll need. It's all here." They drove through the rain and wet streets of town feeling accomplished and respectable. Facing danger and dreams of a better world.

SURREAL   SURREALITY
Tommy K.

Father of Transatlantic cables,
Come to me this mourn
To my mangled birth. You,
Who would take my defications
Fermenting them with your blood wine,
Drinking them during your hallowed sacrifice
Of L.A. policemen not saved for posterity on a cam-
corder.
Come to my coronation,
Mothers of malt liquor brew and whiskey,
Hallower of sacred hangovers
Come to you *Favored Son,*
Whose Lord calls him Father, Son,
High Priest, and Lover.
Come.
Tiller of souls, whatever you be
Come, learn the final lesson,
To be free of this unholy mating of technology with
man
Learn peace,
While slashing your throat and ripping your intestines
out
With a cocktail fork,
Youll see Me in my unholy glory
Ambered cloak of glistening flesh
You recognize,
as your own.

REBIRTH

Tommy K.

All is darkness
there is no light from the flame,
within the mind.
there is no peace
all the crying, the tears,
calling from the past.

Nightwind calls out,
through the twilight of the years,
to the future,
circling me,
beckoning me to follow
leaving all I hold behind.

Eyes of ancients
mirror all my inner truth
all my beliefs.
riding the air,
holding to all the shadows,
to all the elders of the past.

All these feelings
clutching to live in the mind
wishing for birth.
all I shall see,
watching from across the void
when I walk the wind.

OCTOBER 20, 1992

Tommy K.
for Candy M.

What is there to do to day?
driving to and from
walking the same way to 203
Chance matters!!
Oh so ever unseen.....
one phone call before....
Pain...
Silence spiced with rage
(controlled)
finish my route,
Breakdown..

Get away from me!!!!
all you who come
with false wishes of comfort.
Whose masks of understanding
are made of lies, deceit,
and bitter consolation.
Leave!!!
Leave me with my anger
towards this bastard God
Who practices genocide.
God,
Whose saints preach some great grandeur
to be perfect in His eyes
that which they can never be.
Please Leave!!
leave me to console.

My silence
of not returning to see her;
my ring to her
hers to me.
An exchange

silenced by Death
a bitter brother
Whose arms of comfort I welcome
to strip my flesh
to hang on hooks.
My form
dangling,
unstruggling anguish
crucified.

NO NONE

Tommy K.

No

whatever

whats the difference

none i see,

you?

i?

who cared

not i

resistance

a world

alone

forever

cosmos

in a plane

without.

LYING ON THE ALTER

Tommy K.

Lying on the alter
seeking my reason
finding nothing
a void
rolling
my mind
chasing insanity
the only solution
to calls
from below
screams from above.

My Father!!!
my heart,
being
begotten through deception
Hells greatest augury
as the rise
Archangel,
my brother
of the Great
cataclysm
a war,
over this charade
religion leading to destruction
of many races
cultures,
in name of god
genocide.

BLACK OUT   MOUNTAIN

Tommy K.

Now and then I am allowed
to return to my forty
this serenity born of the soul
which may be mine, but is
still a place I long to be.

It is mine, loved by me heart
a myriad of feelings folded in,
as beer batter fried fish.
Made in a place formed of light
(Budlight) where no shadows
of hangovers fall.

Where for my heart beats blindly,
at the likeness of this necromantic shade
whose form resembles my beloved.
This beloved figure, Queen of the Ditch
where visitors frolic in drunken rapture
till their bodies fold.

You say it is only a dream,
empty bottles from an endless source
before the suns morning rise,
What secrets these hills could tell,
drunken frolicking of many nations.

Now and then I am allowed
to return to my forty
as if it were an assurance
to a fragile mind,
a barrier against insanity,

A place which may herald the future
forever picture
of what may be.

SHOWING   EXPRESSIONS

Tommy K.

Showing expressions
little faith
in my being
your pearly whiteness
innocence?
can it be?
Further from the truth
my picture
so distorted
reframed,
my piece of mind.

Your eyes
showing
a window?
Yes,
oblivion
untrusting
so changed
from the first world
of you and i.

Severed be the ties
you bonded
me
so shallow
sorrow
hollow
is your name.

SITTING, LISTENING

Tommy K.

      Sitting, listening
looking out the window
blankly.
watching clouds, cotton puffed
children
playing in the breeze
up there,
How is my sister?
I miss her so
she's been gone so long
where is she?

      This day,
moving
as trees dance
to the hidden music
nature's harmony.
sprouting upwards
little tree
stretch, reach
your life depends
unlike ours,
futile
as the days grow shorter

      All this time
moving
as we
to a purpose?
no
I guess
where is mother?
has she been home,
today?
we were to go
shopping
a last time

        The mirrored waters
a well
of time
seen
yet unreachable
without a bucket
as life is
to us
without imagination.
        who can say
do
to make us
remember
our past
illusion
an increasing dream
in the mind
lost
as i
in haziness.
        Still,
we try
to find a way
to an ending
always knowing
it comes
darkness
as we were born
all
dying

WAITING HURRIEDLY

Tommy K.

Waiting hurriedly
eyeing peace
piece?
a small portion
shallow
as faith
in a bastard god
fallen
yes
as angel
of the Morning
Morning star
deceiver
my Lord
waiting
as i
for mysteries
past the darkness
pain
everlasting
pleasure
received
my punishment
for you.

NAVAJO, a name - Diné, a people

Mark Keiser

I am, identified by a name
so many take for granted, hidden beneath
red stones and sepia ravines, washes of
cool rain, the smell of rain, a Mother Rain
Father Sky, I am given
names you take for granted
the Spider Woman spun a web
pulling stars from the night, to
warm fires fed in the hearth
under the breaking dawn, we pray
acknowledgement of who we are and
appreciation for what we are given, placement
of people, to reserves, our land, Mother Earth
a name given to us,
Tótsoniih dóó Taachiníí, my name
my people, not taken for granted

we are of this land, still
misplaced with a name, small imprints
of the past, ruins resumed
from smoke filled eyes and cactus
splintered fingertips, broken ladders and cliff dwellers
mural walls of death in
Massacre Cave,
in Del Muerto, the air
a home beneath a juniper shower and the red waters
of De Chelly, remind me of who I am

ON COMMON GROUND

Mark Keiser

How can I put it,   into words- appreciation
To remember, we sat under sunrise clouds, prismed
    colors
smeared against a canvas sky, with the dull of our
    brushes
we painted distinct images into velvety hues, cured
purple smoke rings and nicotine ceremonies,
    worshipped
cigarette goddesses, plumed serpents and gave thanks
    by means of
tobacco, offering in blue ashtrays, there
leafy umbrellas hand, a green parasol
breached from smoldering light, to fireflies that
    whisper
in our ears and a flutter of honey wings, taste sweetens
tea seipped from porcelain cuplets we shard, as dusk
breath, fill lungs that of cherry blossoms, wine
a toast to yesterday and next time
when we skip fancy on, acid washed stones
into rivers and reservoirs that restor
this peace between us
You
stand out a prominent number, a numeral
among thousands in counting, I can count to ten
you taught me to use my fingers, to paint images into
    velvety hues
and spin words that stage spindles to create lyrical
    movements,
on paper, I engross my thoughts to lectures, you talk a
    strong tongue
one day we will be able to talk again and use the same
    language,
through this, we can never part
because we are brothers

P.S. REMEMBER THESE

Mark Keiser

I can recall
the smell of baked honey breads
and the familiar scent of pitch pine
a sticky freshness
binding in my hair
and in between my fingers
I use this to stick photographs
of you on my walls
while the burn of incenses
intwines with the smolder of
sleeping sage
that seem ot veil
these pictures of you

I draw the curtains
to flush out
nicotine smoke
and drunkenness of yesternight
All the sunlight to come in
make haste
for the breeze that permits me
to bear i mind
those moments I
had referred to you
as Father   and
adoptig
his name
I could have said
I never remembered these things
but I would only be lying

I can familiarize myself
with these images
the hotdog barbeques

banana cream pie
spilled cool-aid
soaked up by forgiven laughter
Monday night football
Beer
you-

Sometimes these pictures of you
dwindle and fall back
I play upon them
so that I may recapture
times you said to me
I miss you/I wish you were here...
hang up feelings
by a   click
dead dial tone

I want to come home

OF THE GATHERED

Mark Keiser

birds depart, after their songs are heard
after the last summer sun has risen
when the autumn moon, no light
beckons the birds
once more, to sing her to sleep
dreaming forward, under aspen
where eyes see signals and a beacon
shows no warning
when the wind
shift tides , east is remembrance
to the west, trees
long to feel the song of the bird, waiting
return impression far from touch
too close to notice, silencing of birds
create language among the trees, along a remain
leaves left on gelid ground
wind through shallow past
path between dormant
the sky has fallen tomorrow, into november
page inside thought, black birds of metamorphosis
are not what they appear to be, silence
left for the forest to beckon passions song
of the birds, in silence among the trees, among
the moon
whose light diminishes
leaves that cease to fall
with birds circling the dark pines
above, finding an escape from
                                        silence
                        rescuing the night
                swarming transformations of
            black birds,   silenced within

I STOLE HIS PERFUME

Tomomi Kumakura

I stole his perfume
for my wrist

He is like music of unconsciousness.

Stars and flowers make his body.

His perfume make a halo

His mouth is like a baby.
His eyes are so sly, sweet immaculate
His hair of royal blood,
The survivor of the fallen empire.

He drew a picture of
a woman in the nude.

If she is me , I am so glad, and
I stole his perfume.

Tomomi K

熊倉智美

LEFTOVERS

Ruth Mustus

Cannot forget, not wanting to remember but
being chased in my mind until my heart
explodes with the rhythm of rage and
tomorrow.

dancing alone in a room full of unknown
the room in his portrait is depicted alone,

finding fault in the light, changes, charges,
and then is missed by the first
waiting and hoping a misguided taste of
saline and tempera
the eastern sleeps in my mouth
and the after taste of licorice.
Broken by the longing
in hands
fingers and claws
shred my image and I imagine better splinters of my
spirit
and reassemble in a collage, leftovers.

#2

Hearing hollow headed literazzi
espouse the virtuoso
who climbs the heights amongst rungs built upon
blood of bones
engineer emote, manipulating mind montage
a puppet who pulls the strings
and color in a box
white man sun ray
intellectual conceit
pretender pride.
Can I sell you some deep?

picture problem
urban.

A starving child, a three-legged dog, a car wreck
from Saturday night's bingo. Raw chapped wrists
and
a head full of lice?
You, Rez,
you?
antiquated artifacts, brooks brothers, and
11 pairs of black shoes.
The kind I wanted when they teased me
for wearing mocs.
Shiny   shiny wishful Patents.
Any of your friends F.A.S.?
cirrhosis killed my grandma
cops my grandpa.
Have you   ever hid?
under a bed
when they came home
away from the monster your favorite uncle had
become?
I know
you
  DO hide.

OH FATHER

Ruth Mustus

Forgive me for I have
sinned
and then
sinned again.

>   What have you
>   my child

It has been a long time since
my last
confession

>   when did you
>   my child

It seems like forever

>   the lord is patient

I have committed the most
abhorring of all the cardinal sins

>   he will forgive

I am so distressed I think
I can no longer
tolerate myself
I am riddled with guilt

>   cleanse yourself

I fear No one will understand
forget
or forgive

the lord will always love
you

I am not worthy

The lord thinks you are

He will not accept me
no one will
once they find out the truth

My child I cannot help
unless you tell me what

Far too heinous
I must go
should I not be here
me thinks this is so

Wait
wait, let me help you
you will not be judged
let me hear you

Forgive me father
for I have sinned
I

yes?

I wore my Birkenstocks
with my Ralph Lauren Polo
I
did not mean to
i-i-it-it was an accident

221

I swear
I did not intentionally, nor
would I ever do this
Please forgiveme

You will be forgiven
perhaps if you say 12
Hail Marys

And?

if you make a
contribution to a
worthy charity, say
the men's movement,
only when this is done
will you be absolved.

IN VASE

Julia Nathanson

Tall straight
green spikes
rising
out of glass
cylindrical.

Buds tight
strain to explode
color
passion
when ready.

I HEARD A KNOCK AT THE DOOR

Julia Nathanson

I heard a knock
at the door.
It was the old dog
thumping her tail
wanting to come in.
Occasionally
we'd let both
come in
for human contact
before turning in
for the night.

I led them
into the room
and made them sit
on the small rug
swatting them
with a newspaper.

This night they settled quickly
the old one
curled up in a ball
her arthritic legs
tucked under her
twitching
and trembling.
The other
her legs stretched out
eyes closed
in deep sleep.

I sat and sipped
my coffee
glancing at

the television screen
wondering
at their abandonment
of watchfulness.

I thought
how early
in the morning
the older one
heaves herself up
and stands
shaking
hesitating to move
into the cold
and how the other
chasing birds
and rabbits
barks and dances
around her
until she wobbles out
into the air.

And how
they keep in sight
of one another
and bother me
if one is missing
usually locked
and forgotten
inside the garage.

While on the screen
a child of Somalia
dies
at her mother's breast

and elsewhere
men
who once were neighbors
shoot each other
in their streets
where earlier
the General kept the peace.

In their ordinary lives
did they have dogs?

LATE NIGHT VISION
Pat Natseway

The other night, while watching a family reunion on t.v., I thought about how long it had been since I'd seen mine. My living room became blurry, and I fell into the changing colors of one of the glowing phosphorous dots on the screen . . .

When I saw the figure through the haze I knew my time was at hand. He sat cross-legged with his back against a wall next to a great cave. My eyes looked into the deepness of the cave. It called me, told me to go inside. The time was not at hand, it said. Let me warm you from the cold fog and the harsh light. Something, from my fingertips, from the soles of my feet, from a small capillary next to my heart and my heart itself, from the lens in my eye and the tissues that connected both sides of my brain, told me to hold my ground.

The cave was now the rock house I grew up in, and from the doorway my mother's voice came calling. Son, she said, I'm so glad to see you. I turned my head away. It was hard. Your grandfather is waiting, she continued. He has some things to say to you. You know he has been here for a long time. You need to speak to him. Son, do what you must, but do not break his heart.

Tears ran down my face. I wanted to run to her, hold her, and be safe. I knew if I looked up I would have to. Damn me! I closed my eyes and felt myself shrinking down, down, until I thought I might not even recognize myself and then I was sitting alone with the figure and the cave.

Another voice called to me. This time it passed from a kiva opening. It was Sung'aya, the medicine man . . . my own grandfather.

Hey! Don't be scared! he called out. I'm here. Remember the things I said to you, taught you. I showed you the nature of things during your changing. And now you know how it is.

Son, listen to your heart. Do not let it ache so. Use the power of your inner being. Help yourself to understand. I have other things to teach you. We can drink hohoysi tea and discuss it in my kiva. We can pray . . . and we can sing.

I thought about the songs we had sung together. They made me feel like a part of the earth itself. When we sang we were as one: the earth, my grandfather, and I. From those times, I received the help to carry on. Yet, I was in a place that was not the earth. In fact, I felt very far away from it. I allowed myself to move closer to his trusted voice. No more waiting. It was real this time.

I looked up to see flames burning my grandfather's flesh. Lines in his face, the curve of his eyebrows, and the shadows of his long hair were held in disbelief before they were taken over. The flames came closer and overtook me. I saw the last of his organs bubbling in dark blood before my own vision failed in the pain red-yellow of heat.

Once again, I sat alone with the figure and the cave.

Why do you hesitate? asked the figure.

Because I doubt the reliability of my actions, I told him.

Yet, you deny yourself the things you love because of one impulse.

What are the things that you love?

Love is like any other emotion. To tie things to it only makes you weak and confused.

It is meant to be simple, then.

I suppose.

Tell me, do you have a soul?

I have many souls.

Then, you know what love is.

I know what it is, and what it is not. I know it lies inside the cave. And I offer it to you. Turn the cave into anything you want. And, by me, you will know its "true" nature.

I will only go if you come with me. For only you know best your creation.

No! My place is here, by the cave. Surely, you know everything has its place.

Then, I will pray for you, spirit, because you know love, but do not want it.

I lifted myself up and turned. I called the faith in my heart to get me moving. With only the inability to see where I was going, I walked. It felt good to travel again.

WALKING BOY

Pat Natseway

The boy was looking for something. What it was *exactly* he didn't know. But that was no matter to him. He just kept walking along the sandy road, trying to be as observant as possible.

His brother had told him that they lived on the most powerful land in the world. There was a place north of their village called Black Mesa, which was known to be the center of the universe, or so he said. Our tribe, he went on, had come to this place through a hole in the ground, and they had been all over the world. And the only reason they were allowed to live here was because they promised to take care of the land. Never forget that, he added. It would be worse than breaking your mother's heart. Nothing is more true than the very sand you walk on.

Presently, the boy came upon two juniper trees growing across each other on opposite sides of the road. He thought, *How odd it would be if that once I pass the trees I came upon a village from a long time ago. What would I say? I can't even speak my language that well. They would probably laugh at me like the kids at school and say bad things I can't understand. Maybe not. Maybe they were a lot more kind then. If they were, I would never come back.* He walked on and passed the trees. Nothing happened.

He heard stories about certain trails that led to different places. One went to Dog Village, which sat atop a mesa that had cliffsides as smooth as glass. Another went to the house of Spider Grandmother and the Twin War Gods. There was even one that went to Maski, the land of the dead. *Would I be lucky to find one?* he thought. *No, I better not. I don't have any paahos to give to the guardians of the trails, and there's sure to be some.*

A cool breeze swept across his brow and

played with the thin hairs that grew above his forehead. It felt good, so he stopped and took a deep breath to celebrate. He wondered if it might have been a spirit making its way across the mesa. *How much better it must feel to be able to float through air and play among the clouds,* he thought. *I would spend my time talking with the rocks and playing with children of the north winds.*

He continued walking on, noting the particular sounds of birds, and once scaring a cottontail, which ran leaving a small cloud of dust. Every now and then, the breeze would pick up and tousle his hair and create waves in his T-shirt. He felt an urge to take off his sneakers and feel the earth under his feet, so he did. Once through, he gazed into the sky, catching the silent flight of a blue jay. *Blue has to be the best color. I wonder if Taawa made the corn blue to remind us of the sky. I'll ask Kwa'a about it. He would be the one to know those things, 'cause I know if I ask taha, he'll just want me to hoe his weeds for him. One time he said my hair grew like weeds and he was going to cut it. No way! I will never let him cut it. He was just honakiwta, anyway. I can out run him any day.*

He laughed to himself a little, then started on his way again, dragging his feet through the soft sandy patches when he came upon them. He avoided the small rocks, and remembered his mom telling him one time that when she was small her feet had grown a very thick skin, and she could step on rocks and stickers and bullheads and they would never hurt her. *Iss ana! For me, the stickers would have no mercy. They'll stick me all over and I'll go crying home. No way! I'll get matches and burn them! Ha!*

He now neared the end of the road, which was also the tip of the mesa. When he reached the edge, he looked down and down and down, then back up to the horizon. The mesa had not entirely ended, only the top part where he now stood. There was another plateau underneath, which went on a little further before also ending at a cliff, a jumble of rocks and boulders flattening out to the bottom of the valley. He noticed a huge cube of rock sitting on the second tier and thought it looked very strange to be there by itself. *Don't worry, mister o'wa. I'll come down to visit you.*

After putting his shoes back on, he found a place on the ledge to lower himself down, past the boulders that had fallen off the edge, being careful not to scrape his knees on the rough surfaces, and traveled towards the big rock. He came upon it from its shady side and walked around it, hoping to find a place to climb up. What he saw on the sunny side made him stop and drop his lower jaw.

The lit rock face was covered with writing and pictures. Even high up, where it seemed no one could possibly reach, there were lines and shapes. There were faces, people, plants, and other symbols all carved and etched into the surface. *A story! Someone has written a story!*

He climbed up to it and touched a line which formed a snake. It felt warm and very old. He remembered his grandfather telling him that every person walks a different path on the earth and each one has a unique way of talking to it. That's one of the reasons why we are able to live here, he said, because we listen and find out what the land needs. Then we give to it and it returns our crops. *I wish I knew what this rock is trying to say. It's old, like my kwa'a. I wonder if he knew it when it was just a small rock. He might even know the story!*

He stared intently at the figures for a while, then, very slowly, placed his ear against them. Concentrating, he listened for something, anything.

He thought he heard it singing.

UNTITLED

Maxine Perkins

Alone
Dark room
  one beam of light
She holds black and white
  that's aged and torn
Doesn't blink
  memorizing every line,
   crease, every facial feature
hypnotized self   to creep
  inside your head
erasing
       slowly
           fading out
all the bad memories
you've hidden through
boyish smiles

KAHENTEWAKS: She Shakes the Grass

Maxine Perkins

Gas mask over my mouth
was all he saw
I wonder if it's 75 degrees
outside today?
Please go wait in the Cathedral
was all he heard me say.
Waiting was all he could do...
A minute before the arrival
He wrote:
When you were born I saw
hail, wind, rain and lightning
I heard your mother cry
and the thunder rumble
All these things are strong
sure and true
as is your stubbornness
Your mother suffered as greatly
as her love is for you
Thank you for coming this day.

I WILL LIVE

Maxine Perkins

I will live
until there is
nothing
to live
for

I will die
because there is
nothing
to live
for
anymore

although there is one way into
death
there is also a way out...

When my soul comes to claim me,
I will put on my happiest face,
and wear my best dress.

BLACK DRESS
Melissa A. Pope

Tight
As a black dress
She is
Dressed
in dream, entangled, in day

she knows how to get
one night stands

she knows what she wants
bring my fine wine to sip

she knows shat she wants
light my candles and cover me in my comforters

she knows what she wants
take me to my place, take me there right now

give me your paintings for my bare walls
give me your words for my empty envelopes
tell me of your admiration
for my dancing arms, my monkey lips, and nappy hair
tell me how beautiful I am
they all do

Tight
As a black dress
She is
Worn
In dreams, entangled, in dark

she knows how to get
ALL THAT
she doesnt want

restless in   her actions
restless in   her dreams
where no one can reach her self sought tightness

UNCOMFORTABLY DRY

Melissa A. Pope

I.

I walked in the basement with grey lockers and eye
stinging lights on the ceiling as a boy dressed in polo
gave me a side look before he closed the door behind
him as I looked for security in the empty corridors
unashamed to cry only tired of crying and finding
blank people consumed by mirrors

II.

I watched myself in the mirror while I sat in the front
with the window rolled up to keep out the dry bitter
cold in the sunny afternoon on my way to the hospital
with tense muscles and a complection that showed the
thoughts in my youth at the drive through of
McDonalds.

6:37 am

Melissa A. Pope

I watched the shadows of light
shadows of morning
enter the single room
they land on the rug
as soundless as snow
that falls to cover the ground
as we covered
wrapped in black and white stripes
of cotton
while his leg rested on mine
he watched in silence
in the grey haze of morning
my eyes could feel the snow falling
and I could feel how old it was

TONIGHT

Melissa A. Pope

for my next thought
I will let my palm sweat then open
to the air
to the breeze going through my fingers
my lines of fortune
cooled beside the tree
that grows behind my purple curtain that hangs
by the light of my candle
and how I see through
where the curtain won't reach
to the tree I never sat by

THE FLUTE

Melissa A. Pope

green, yellow and red
blades of tall grass had grown
blowing sunlight through
down a steep bank
she followed
the canoe path
by the flambeau river
they sat on the river rocks
with muddy feet
half hanging in the familiar
currents
where plants grew widely
and tall tree leaves
stood from roots down below
elegantly
they were
twelve or thirteen
and she felt the short moss
carpet under her hand
and ankle
under her breath
the still air carried
the notes played
as fish in sunless currents
swam upstream
his flute music
played for her
carried by
stretched along

GERANIUM

Heidi Rankin

I dream of the red geranium
veiny leaves of scalloped edge
round red petals of individual blossoms
making up the whole
larger flower.
dry and yellowed leaves
I pluck
lessen the drain on the living.

RED AND OCHRE, UMBER LEAVES

Salome Starbuck

Red and ochre,umber leaves
blowing
cold autumn light pavement
and the smell of moisture in the rotting soil
hail rattling on my bathroom sky light at four in the
    morning
rattling
The pale white light on the window pane behind you,
    as you sip coffee,across the table,looking beyond me
the smell of oil paint and turpentine on my hands,dry
    and cracked
and the Crotchety Man who I serve a pastry and a cup
    of coffee to,and the way my Papa makes time,now
    that he is leaving
resting
in cadmium light, the glaze of color left like a film over
    my eyes
and the way I can't see beyond the notes of memory
in fall
when the patterns on my quilt remind me
and the wind in the east window blows the paper
    shades,and the steam radiator gurgles,hisses,and
    pops at me all night the rattling rain on my skylight,
    and the rhythms of the high door frames,old
    victorian doorknobs etched with vines,and the lines
    of the wood floors running north-south appease me
and the spaces fill with blood or
afternoon light on the floor
and I wonder if home replaces the ache
as the red and orange leaves on washed out white
    pavement replace the reflectiveness of your skin
the reflectiveness absorbed into the rising mist of
    dusk,decay,and the green sweater I wear when I
    say goodbye

ENWRAPT

Salome Starbuck

enwrapt
in a dream
and cotton
diffuse underskin glow
radiating
from you
like an overcast sea
light from my window
skin reflecting
morning
i am watching your eye lids
flicker
watching the changes
in time
tension between the day we
sat on the steps and
fell into a reverie
the night we had tea
in my room
until five in the morning
not speaking
and they way i sip coffee, now
while you sleep
light
caught between
solitude
and the taste of your skin

TEMPESTUOUS PIT

Carlson N. Vicenti

Vast empty miles
and streets traveled
unmeasurably cold time
dripping
wasted
blank
drained
uninhabited
wandering vacant alleys
pissing   puking   drinking
polluting bars.
Black snow falling
bombarding
fourteen winters
linked.
Flakes melt
warm urine and stale beer.
Swirling cesspool
pulls me
to current center,
into depression.
I stagger, spinning.
side-stepping broken bottles,
crushed cans and shattered dreams.
I slide deeper and deeper,
clinging to slick leathery walls
of cirrhotic livers.
Coagulating hangover saliva
oozes from the walls.
I lose my grip
and stumble down.
Screaming beaten wives
and F.A.S. children crying,
counting down steps in the abyss.

I bounce and bounce,
each collision sounds like
dry heaves.
I struggle to keep my balance,
but fall, fall and fall,
deeper and darker,
to slam heavily on my back,
rock bottom.

I wake as a child crying,
hollow, alone, shivering cold
heart and spirit
gone.
It is dark,
black black.
The air is stagnant,
sour and putrid,
like puked up blood and stomach lining.
I am alone, except for
drunken emotions groping at me,
tormenting me.
I try and escape,
but slick walls
offer no hold, and
emotions jerk me back.
Fear tears out my liver,
it burns like alcohol on a cut.
Envy prances around me
dropping insults.
Jealousy embraces a beautiful Greed,
adorned in rubies and gold.
Sadness holds me down,
and Selfishness encourages Hatred
to brutalize me.
Everclear burns from my eyes,

But nobody hears my mental agony.
I resign myself to die
in oblivion.
I lay down,
close my eyes,
kicked repeatedly unconscious.

A voice wakes me.
A star whispering,
Come, I'll give you a way out.
Delicate sparkling strand of silk
descends.
I climb.
Emotions waken and attack.
I kick Fear aside,
shaking free from Greed, Jealousy, and Envy.
I leave Abandon, Misery, and Despair.
Selfishness, Sadness, and Hatred cling.
I fight every inch of the climb,
higher and higher, until
the star is no longer small,
it is the sun rise.
I hear a drum beating,
in the distance,
it is my heart.
Voices sing within me,
my spirit returns.
Fear, Sadness, and Hatred
cannot live in beauty, let go to fall
back into the tumultuous pit.
I pass uselessness and
the ancient songs pull me back
to where my life began

as a child growing.
It is a long way to climb,
now I climb
unhindered by alcohol.

BESH CHI DAL KAIL
Carlson N. Vicenti

Praise
heaved out   mouths
reflecting voices
bestowing grace
upon wrinkled
white woman.
Strokes of softness
shared images
defiling sacred
land immortal
paintings attempt
to capture
spirit
with brushes.
pastel flowers
her reputation,
Santa Fe style
nauseating
creator
mountain's essence
lives free
without borders
of canvas   stonehenge
and photographs.
High above
mortal breaths
Monster Slayer's
resting place
transmitted in   background
of entertainment   transparencies.
Southwest
haven of
artistes
violating visions

extending distances
horizons close
where white folk
from New York
should remain,
abandoning beauty
untouched by muse.
Ranch of ghosts
cavernous mouth
resound curses
of ancestors
in me.
to hell
you fall
Georgia
O'Keefe.

DARKNESS WANDERING

Carlson N. Vicenti

Darkness
             Star

Thoughts of you, walk
silently through my mind.
Kicking doors, to rooms, open
to find empty.
Emotions wander
deserted paths, that
lead to your door.

Dream clouds
carry your image,
into the distance, where
you sleep alone.
I see the child
in delicate lines
on your face.
Empty clouded sky
in your eyes,
shrouds your smile.
Your songs
deceive sorrow
with voices
of love.

Stars
             Wink

tears of loneliness.
To be away from you,
I wake shivering
in an empty bed,
hugging a pillow
of stone.